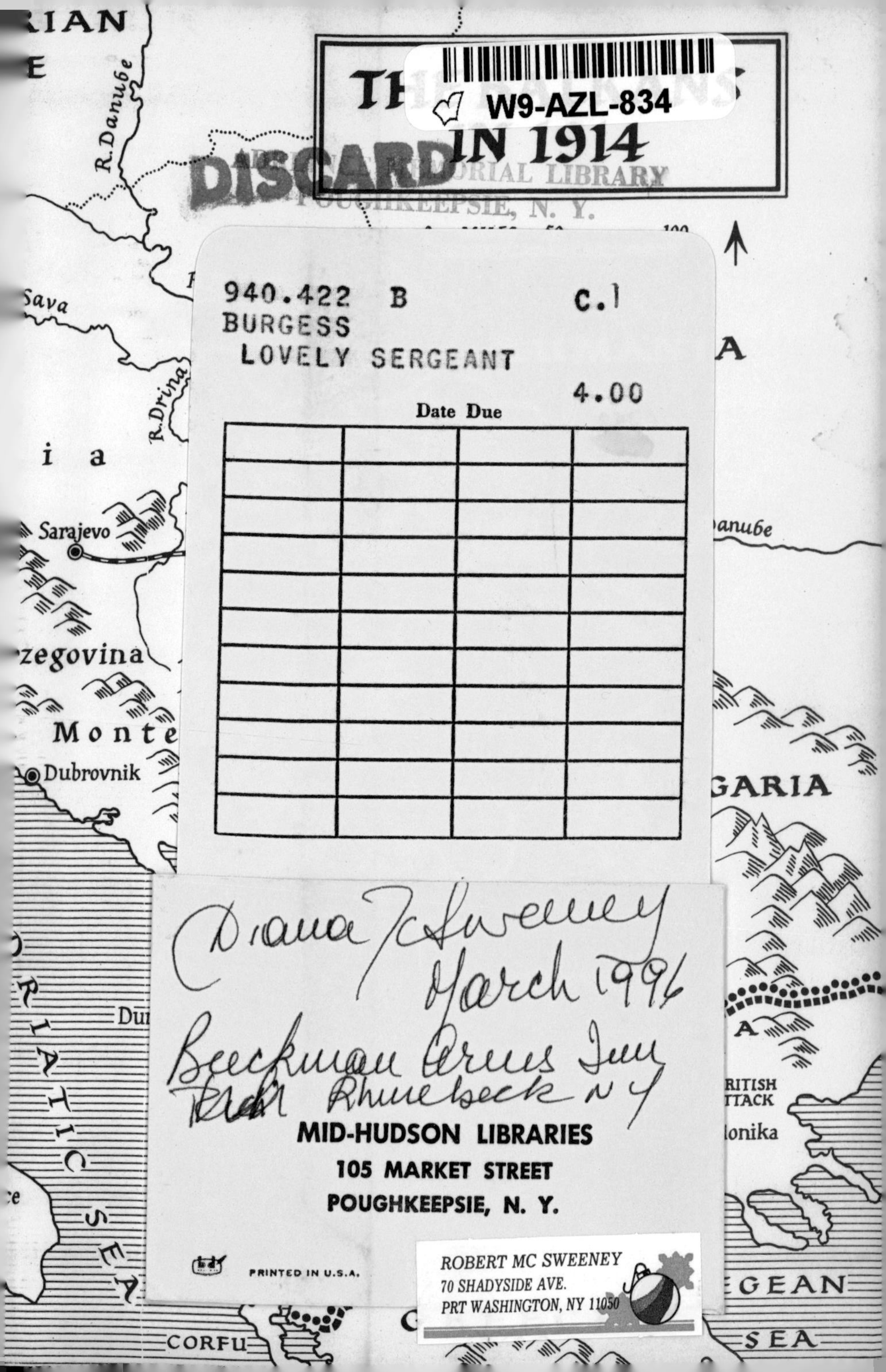

W9-AZL-834
DISCARD
ADRIANCE MEMORIAL LIBRARY
POUGHKEEPSIE, N. Y.
940.422 B C.1
BURGESS
LOVELY SERGEANT
4.00
Date Due
Diana McSweeney
March 1996
Beekman Arms Inn
Rhinebeck NY
MID-HUDSON LIBRARIES
105 MARKET STREET
POUGHKEEPSIE, N. Y.
PRINTED IN U.S.A.
ROBERT MC SWEENEY
70 SHADYSIDE AVE.
PRT WASHINGTON, NY 11050

THE LOVELY SERGEANT

By Alan Burgess

THE SMALL WOMAN

SEVEN MEN AT DAYBREAK

THE LOVELY SERGEANT

Sergeant Flora Sandes plays chess with comrades during a lull on the front

Diana McSweeney
March 96

THE LOVELY SERGEANT

ALAN BURGESS

NEW YORK: E. P. DUTTON & CO., INC.,
1963

Copyright, ©, 1963 by Alan Burgess
All rights reserved. Printed in the U.S.A.

FIRST EDITION

No part of this book may be reproduced in any form without permission in writing from the publisher, except by a reviewer who wishes to quote brief passages in connection with a review written for inclusion in a magazine, newspaper or broadcast.

Library of Congress Catalog Card Number: 62-7062

ACKNOWLEDGEMENTS

I am deeply grateful to Professor S. L. Baker, Mr Gerard Baker, and Miss Dorothy and Phyllis Baker of Orford, Suffolk, for allowing me to read and make use of Flora Sandes's lectures, diaries, letters, albums, and the mass of papers she had gathered over the years. I am also greatly indebted to Mr S. D. Sandes of Fort Victoria, Southern Rhodesia for a great store of personal reminiscences and other material, and to Mrs Vidakavic and Doctor Macphail, two of Flora's closest friends. I would like to thank Oliveria Vojvodic, Nemad Petrovic, and all the other generous people in Yugoslavia who gave me help while I was researching and retracing the routes taken by Flora Sandes. I am also grateful to the Bakers and Mr Sandes for allowing me to reproduce photographs from Flora's album, and to the Imperial War Museum for the others.

Because of the problem presented by the spelling of Yugoslavian place names (the Serbs use a Cyrillic alphabet and the Croats a Latin) I have, in the hope of simple uniformity, resorted to the spelling used in the *Concise Oxford Atlas*.

ILLUSTRATIONS

Prologue

THE SNOW came down obliquely out of the slaty sky, packing into Flora's eyes and mouth and nostrils. Soft and feathery, she could hardly feel it, and soon her body and the entire stretcher were covered by a thick crust of flakes.

At first she found she could still move her left arm. She managed to get it up to her face and tried feebly to brush the snow away. She knew she could expect no help from the bearers wrestling and levering the stretcher down the mountainside. But she tired quickly of her exertions. Besides, the snow was now falling too heavily.

She closed her eyes again. She lay there and allowed the snow to cover her face, but still there was no peace. The effect of the brandy was wearing off now, and the whole of her right side was beginning to hurt again.

She knew simply that she was going to die. After all, she *had* been a nurse, and she *had* been in action long enough to know that you couldn't be as badly wounded as this and survive the agonizing descent to the first aid post.

Now, too, she was feeling the cold. It was creeping up from her feet to her knees and into her thighs. She felt the orderlies set down the stretcher, wedging it in the snow. A rough hand brushed the flakes from her face. A stubbly chin appeared. She felt breath on her cheek. He'd drunk some of the brandy too. She was not surprised when he began to tell her that they were lost. She had suspected as much for the past half-hour.

He was very apologetic. The driving snow had obliterated every track and every landmark, he explained. They could not see more than ten yards. They had not the slightest idea where the hospital tent was; they might be going in the wrong direction entirely; they might be heading for the Bulgarian lines for all he knew. They'd stumble on for another fifteen minutes or so, try and find shelter under a rock or in a cave, waiting for the blizzard to blow itself out. It was all very unfortunate.

Flora nodded dumbly. She knew that if they had to shelter, she would be denied even the comparative luxury of dying in the warmth of the hospital tent.

Was she all right, he asked anxiously. Flora tried to form words, but her lips would not co-operate, so she nodded once again, feeling sorry for the stretcher-bearers. Her company would hold them responsible for losing her. The men she had left fighting so desperately up on the mountainside would want to know what had happened to her. She was not being conceited. The face of Sergeant-Major Milosh, tears streaming down his cheeks as they carried her away, had revealed as much.

It was really incredible. A Serbian sergeant-major of the old school, a man who had survived so many vicious battles against the Turks and Bulgars, and a score of bloody hand-to-hand engagements with bayonet and knife, was weeping like a schoolboy because he thought she was done for! She had hardly ever seen him smile, let alone cry!

She felt them lift her and they lurched downwards again. The stretcher jerked and she bit her lower lip.

What had Lieutenant Doditch said it was? A grenade. A grenade which had struck the revolver in her belt and exploded. If that was true she certainly had no right to be alive, even this long. She must accept these extra hours as a special dispensation from God. Maybe the time was given to her so that she could reflect upon her sins. Certainly Janachko, with his blinding religious certainty would have thought so. Lieutenant Janachko Jovitch where was he now? Still in the valley of the 'Sweet Flower'? She yearned for the comfort of his presence, even for an hour, even for a minute.

That charge had taken them right in amongst the Bulgars. It had seemed for a moment as if that secret nightmare of hers—the bloody cut and thrust of naked bayonet—had become real. She had seen the Bulgars ten yards ahead. She had seen them in the mist, seen their arms swing back to throw the grenades. And then that great orange flash.

Anyway, they wouldn't have her body to mutilate. Like Lemuel, she would be found dead on the battlefield, if not 'within the enemy lines', then at least honourably close to them. How did the epitaph go upon the alabaster memorial in that Saxon church?

'Lemuel Shuldham, cornet in the Scots Greys, the younger of

the two sons of William Shuldham of Marlsford Esq., and Mary his wife . . . born on the 27th February . . . fell in battle on the eighteenth of June 1815 at Waterloo . . . Far in advance within the sight of the French lines his body was found next morning and buried on the spot.'

Quickly her mind leapt back to the square-towered, flintstone church which had stared for a thousand years across the fields and hedges, woods and dales, towards the grey and windy Suffolk sea. In the spring, when the windows were open, she used to smell the fresh-cut grass scythed round the gravestones out in the churchyard, saw the daffodils like little yellow flames against the dim altar, and heard Papa's voice droning endlessly on about how blessed were the pure in heart, and how the meek would inherit the earth. At these moments the wide eyes of ten-year-old Flora had crept round to re-read that inscription upon the alabaster memorial. 'Lemuel Shuldham, cornet in the Scots Greys . . .' It was like the beginning of a beautiful psalm. She would go off in a colourful dream of cannons belching flames and smoke, and of scarlet-coated dragoons firing with courge and precision at the thundering French cavalry charges. When Flora got to her feet to sing the hymn, 'All things bright and beautiful', her heart had bled for poor Lemuel out there on the battlefield all by himself and grievously wounded, and when she blinked back the tears and Mama patted her approvingly upon the shoulder, touched that one so young should be moved by simple piety, Flora was at the head of her platoon, bearing a defiant Union Jack, fighting desperately through the thick of the battle to reach his side.

Oh, it was so long ago now. Before the turn of the century her father, the Reverend Samuel Dickson Sandes, had become rector of the tiny village of Marlsford in Suffolk—a brass plate upon the wall still recalls his benevolent tenancy—and she had grown up in the old stone vicarage, youngest of a family of five boys and three girls.

They used to explore the meadows and lanes right down to the misty coastline of Aldeburgh and Orford. In winter they saw the wild ducks rise in percussive flights from the ice-encased marshes; on summer evenings the scents of honeysuckle and new-mown hay pervaded the lanes, and the moon rose behind the tower of the church bright as the newly-minted sovereign the Squire put in the plate every Christmas morning.

Could she ever forget those endless sunny Edwardian afternoons, with the cedar trees casting long shadows across the lawn, the limp tennis rackets looping the scruffy balls across the sagging net, the croquet mallets clicking in aural exclamation marks to the girlish voices raised in ecstasy or anger? In the drawing-room Mama would inevitably be entertaining: a small committee meeting perhaps, or a few ladies of the parish at a sewing-circle. There, amidst the gentle chatter of bone china cups on the silver tray, the muted splash of amber liquid, the tiny quiver of rising steam, the conversation was mandarin in its formality. The Empire was secure, Britain ruled the waves, and only a few radicals doubted that this happy state of affairs could continue for ever.

No one had dreamt then that a perverse and dedicated young Serbian named Gavrillo Princep, standing outside a cake-shop in Sarajevo, would with two fortuitous shots change the pattern of the world for good and all.

She sensed rather than heard the stretcher-bearers' excitement. At first she couldn't understand what they were saying, then the same rough hand scraped the snow from her face and she realised that the blizzard had eased. It was only a temporary lull, but they could see the Field Ambulance tent down to their right. They would reach it within twenty minutes.

Flora hardly remembered her arrival, only the wonderful change from cold to warmth. She saw a face bending over her and recognised her friend Serge Konstantin, the young doctor in charge of the 2nd Regiment's Field Ambulance. His tunic was unbuttoned at the neck, he was unshaven, his overall stained and his eyes bloodshot. He was so unlike the elegant young officer she knew that she hardly recognised him.

'Christ, Sandes!' he said vehemently, 'where have you been?' Weak as she was, Flora could still reflect: what an incredibly stupid question! Where the devil did he think she'd been? Taking a quiet stroll in the snow?

She groaned as they lifted her out of the pool of blood and melted snow in the hollow of the stretcher. They brushed off the snow and wrapped her in warm blankets. Serge Konstantin supported her head and insisted she sip hot tea laced with brandy. As he talked, she understood why he was so agitated.

As soon as the news had reached the Colonel that Sergeant

Sandes was badly wounded, he had rung up the ambulance tent on the field telephone. Where was Sandes? Well, why the hell wasn't she in the tent? It was the doctor's job to find her! He was to send out a two-man patrol at once! Fifteen minutes later, another telephone call. Why no Sandes? Did the doctor expect the Colonel to go and look for her himself? The doctor would send out another patrol at once. What! The doctor couldn't afford to send any more men? Then he must find some; he would go on sending out patrols until Sandes was found! If Sandes wasn't brought in at once someone was going to be court-martialled.

Meanwhile, the orderlies expertly cut away the English-tailored corduroy breeches. Flora glanced down. She felt a wave of nausea. Was that the firm, white, rounded body of which she had been so proud? That torn and bleeding mess stretching from her breast right down to her thigh?

She felt the tears pricking in her eyes, and a sob welling up in her throat. Oh, dammit, she didn't want to cry. She'd slept and eaten and suffered and fought with men. She'd discarded all the feminine refuges; particularly the tears. And now, in spite of her, they were flowing down her cheeks and she was choking with grief. 'Oh, damn,' she sobbed, 'damn!'

She half turned to Konstantin by the operating table, hid her face against his chest and howled. He allowed her the luxury of grief for about ten seconds, before gently lowering her on to her back. With his thumb he made a scooping movement under each eye to remove the tears. He lit a cigarette and stuck it in her mouth.

'Sandes,' he said sternly, 'you know we now have to probe for shrapnel. Act like a soldier.'

Flora sniffed back her tears. It was her own fault. She had wanted to be as good as any man. And so she had. But was there any point in it?

She saw Serge Konstantin turn his back on her. She knew his eyes were searching through that case of surgical instruments for the right probe and the correct forceps. She knew all about them: she'd done the same thing herself on a hundred occasions. The only difference this time was that the instruments were going to be used upon her.

How and why had she ever got mixed up in this business in the first place? It was all that Matron's fault. If that Matron had

had any common sense at all, Flora would now be bustling around some flower-decorated hospital ward, flirting with all the wounded heroes, instead of lying here waiting to die in a draughty tent on the Macedonian mountainside.

Yes, it was all that Matron's fault.

'Now this,' said Serge Konstantin gently, 'might hurt a bit.'

Chapter One

I

THE MATRON sat behind the bare scrubbed table, going through Flora's thin sheaf of St John's Ambulance certificates with an air of almost audible contempt.

Flora looked at her anxiously. If only she would make up her mind . . . Didn't she realise that this was August 1914 and that there was no time to lose?

Her eyes wandered round the huge hospital anteroom. It smelt of carbolic and cleanliness. Outside, a hot August sun burnt down, but the high uncurtained window effectively barred all contamination from the outer world. Through the well-polished panes of glass she could just hear the sounds of horse buses and hansom cabs clip-clopping across Westminster Bridge, and the occasional hoot of a tug passing up the Thames.

At last the Matron looked up. Was this her only nursing experience? she asked.

'I've been training in my spare time for years,' said Flora urgently.

She saw the Matron register polite interest. 'Your *spare* time?' she murmured.

Flora ignored the snub. She kept her tongue and her hasty temper under control, because she wanted desperately to become a real nurse and be sent overseas.

She knew in her bones that this was the vital moment of her life. If she failed now she would always fail, and drift on into genteel middle-aged spinsterhood. She knew she was reasonably pretty, with a fair skin, brown hair and eyes, and a good figure. She was of medium height; she had a firm chin, and in times of trouble she stuck out her full lower lip aggressively. As a small girl she had prayed every night that in the morning she would have turned into a boy. But every morning she would wake up and discover to her disappointment that she was still a girl. It seemed monstrously unfair that so large a proportion of the world's adventure should be open only to men, and, as she grew older and realised that God was not going to change her into a boy, Flora began to make her own plans.

Her idyllic life in the Suffolk countryside ended when she was sent off to a finishing-school in Switzerland. There she learnt excellent French and German, and a variety of things it was thought all young ladies ought to know. Afterwards, on her father's retirement, the family moved to Thornton Heath in Surrey, and she began to earn her own living.

She was strategically well placed to get a job as secretary in London. Female secretaries were very rare indeed in the years preceding the First World War. The family income was not large but a little went a long way; and aunts, uncles and grandparents could be depended upon for small donations at Christmas and birthdays. Her purchase of a second-hand racing car was perhaps her greatest achievement of the period.

It was a French car: a one-cylinder Sizaire-Naudin. Its huge polished brass lamps shone like gold. Its quilted upholstery, built by carriage-makers with generations of experience behind them, was as springy as a king's bed. When you sat behind the massive steering-wheel you felt like the captain of some ocean liner. Under the leather-strapped bonnet throbbed a single-cylinder engine, powerful and resonant. It propelled her along with a roar which had English villagers ducking for cover when she was still a mile away.

Along these dusty English lanes rarely covered with tarmac, the dust marked only by the wheels of bicycles and gigs, carriages and wagons, she drove through Edwardian summer after summer, across an English countryside of changing seasonal loveliness with the proud awareness of a pioneer—and a female one at that—in the new motor age. Open-mouthed old gaffers in smocks and young farmers in breeches watched her pass and wondered what the world was coming to. It was just as well they didn't know.

And now here she was, her future clouded by this angular Matron who thought she lacked *experience*!

Didn't the woman realise that for Flora Sandes this was zero hour? She had abandoned the idea of marriage. Or perhaps she had abandoned the idea of ever finding a man she could fall in love with. She once thought she was in love with Richard, an American naval officer she met in England. He seemed different, there was a touch of the pioneer about him, and, when he formally requested her hand in marriage, it seemed perfectly normal to go to America and consider it. There her doubts had started. In the small naval base on the east coast, she had looked round at the neat little houses, the formal, God-fearing society, the sailors' wives with their sewing-parties and squalling kids, and she had become frightened. It was all right for the men who could just go off to sea and forget it all, but Flora had to live there for ever!

She talked to Richard and he failed to understand. Like all the others he could not fathom why she should rebel from the woman's task of producing babies and looking after men. Flora tried to explain that this might be Nature's idea of continuity, but she thought that her purpose in life should be deeper than that.

Richard didn't see it her way. Flora didn't try and convince him. She fled.

Of course her family had always been concerned about her lack of 'success'. Her father was always producing curates intended as suitable soul-mates. Croquet on the lawn and a curate, that had been the pattern. It had taken Flora all her time to prevent herself hitting some of the idiots over the head with her croquet mallet. All the men she really liked were married already, or intimidated by her exuberant nature.

Flora had decided long ago that, on the whole, men were lucky. They had all the fun. Look at them now. A war had started, due to their complete incompetence, and what were they doing? Trying their hardest to keep women out of it! If they expected her to stay at home and knit socks while they marched off with the bands playing and the flags flying, they were mistaken.

Didn't the Matron understand all this? Wasn't she on the side of the feminine sex after all? Her next words, precise and formal, proved that indeed she wasn't. 'You must understand,' she said, 'that the efforts of the St John's Ambulance and other voluntary organisations, useful though they are, cannot be compared with the work of a great hospital like this one. I understand that you have no experience other than that to which these—er—certificates refer?'

'No,' said Flora unhappily.

There was another long pause. What, thought Flora in despair, do I tell her now? Should she tell her of those evenings, weekends and holidays spent learning to apply splints to healthy legs, and tourniquets to imaginary wounds; those lectures on the antidotes to nose-bleeding, fits, childbirth, electric shocks and drowning? But the certificates had already done that.

Should she tell of her experiences with the Ladies' Nursing Yeomanry? Flora bit her lip reflectively. Better not, perhaps. After all, that doctor hadn't been exactly complimentary, had he?

The exercise had been designed to test the skill and initiative of young ladies both as horsewomen and nurses. A wheeled stretcher was harnessed to each horse. The girls had to ride out, astride the horse, to a wounded man lying upon the field of battle, dress his wounds, place him upon the stretcher, and return to the Field Ambulance tent. Marks would be awarded for speed, skill and overall efficiency.

At the start, Flora jostled for position. As the judge's handkerchief dropped, she was off like a potential Derby winner. Within a hundred yards she led by ten lengths. The wheeled stretcher, bouncing and rattling behind her, seemed on the point of overturning. Within seconds she had selected her 'wounded' soldier, a rather disgruntled Territorial. His 'wounds' were marked in chalk on his uniform and cap; he was apparently suffering from a broken leg and a cut head. Flora rummaged in her kit for splints and bandages. Her first aid completed, she levered him into her stretcher, and trussed him to it. Remounting her horse, she headed enthusiastically back down the home straight.

Flushed, hair awry, eyes bright, knowing that she had beaten every other girl by at least a minute, she confidently awaited the judge's verdict. The doctor judges unbound and unsplinted the private, who went off for a pint and a few pithy remarks to his comrades about what the bleeding army was coming to. The judges made their notes and consulted privately.

Finally, the chairman called for silence and announced the winner. It was not Flora. She was not even placed in the list. She was disqualified. When the tentful of chattering girls had dispersed, the chairman called her aside for a private interview. He was not complimentary. He told her that the object of the exercise was to demonstrate how life could be saved. He could only say that the speed at which she had performed her exercise was more suitable to a point-to-point than a nursing competition. Had the unfortunate private really been wounded, he would venture to observe that her precipitant haste would not only have seriously aggravated his condition, but in all likelihood she would have arrived at the field hospital with a corpse.

Discouraged, Flora left the tent and walked past the refreshment marquee where the private had drunk his first pint, and was now well into his second. He saw Flora and called out to her. 'Miss! Did you get first prize?'

Although she knew a lady simply did not drink in a beer tent with the common soldiery, Flora approached him, glad that he seemed to bear her no malice for his rough ride.

She told him what had happened, and he laughed, and offered to buy her a drink. Instead, Flora bought him one, and buried her own nose in a glass of light ale. She knew it was unladylike, but couldn't stand gassy lemonade.

The memory of cool beer on that faraway afternoon vanished as the cold voice continued. 'No doubt you are acting with the best motives,' it said, 'but you must realise that in this very hospital there are hundreds of young women who, from their earliest years, have devoted their lives to the vocation of nursing. The war will only last until Christmas. There are plenty of trained professional nurses about ready and able to handle all the wounded this war is likely to produce.' The long, bony fingers pushed Flora's certificates back across the table. 'No doubt you will find something else to suit your—er—talents,' she said. 'Good morning—Miss—er—Sandes.'

Flora gathered up her certificates, mumbled her thanks, and made for the door. She had been snubbed. Worse than snubbed—crushed!

Dejectedly, she caught the train back to Thornton Heath. She opened the door of the house in St Paul's Road opposite the church. Her mother had died in 1911 and her father was now almost bed-ridden. He was a patriarchal, kindly man who watched over his sons and daughters with pride and affection. Flora, the youngest, who had arrived so late in his life, had been his favourite and possibly escaped with more tolerance than discipline. Besides Flora, whose interest in housekeeping was non-existent, the household consisted of her sister Fanny, two housemaids, and Cullen and Moffat.

Flora, who couldn't stand female cooks, had recruited Cullen. The former seacook was over seventy, wore a long white beard, and had been a chef most of his life with the Castle Line. He was a very good cook. At sea he used a coal range; his knowledge of gas-stoves was limited. Shortly after his arrival he turned on a gas-tap, wandered off to get a light, did something else, and eventually returned carrying a lighted taper. The explosion blew the old man flat on his back, singed his beard, and sent the panes of the kitchen windows cascading into the apple orchard.

Moffat, who was Irish, and had acted as her father's butler, confidant, nurse, secretary, and *agent provocateur* for many years, said it served the old fool right. They were seen later, however, discussing the evils of the world over a bottle of whiskey. Moffat believed vehemently that a trust in God and a good bottle of Irish whiskey were proof against most mortal and spiritual enemies.

Annie, one of the housemaids, who had 'done' for the Sandes family ever since Flora could remember, possessed no such convenient faith. She was of indeterminate age. Her face was scrawny, her greying hair untidy, and her black uniform, white apron and cap, always looked as if they had been slept in.

Now she eyed Flora suspiciously as she came in through the front door, and Flora recognised the look. Annie suspected 'sin' in every human being. Anyone who visited that unholy place known as London was suspect of having at least brushed up against it.

She had news for Flora. That 'Mrs-what's-her-name' from the Red Cross Branch had called. Apparently a 'Mrs-somebody-or-other' was trying to get up a party of nurses to go out to Serbia with her. They had to leave within a week. This Red Cross person wondered if Flora might be interested.

Annie went on to say how she had told 'Mrs-what's-her-name' that she thought the whole idea was absolutely mad, and how she was sure Miss Flora wouldn't entertain it for a second, but Flora was hardly listening. A chance to get into the war? An opportunity to become a nurse in the very country where the war had started? It sounded wonderful.

She cut off Annie in mid-flow, saying emphatically that as far as she was concerned she thought it a marvellous idea. What was more, she was going around straight away to ask the Red Cross Organiser if she thought she might have a chance of joining the party. Studying Annie's face as she closed the front door, Flora thought how nice it would have been if she could have thought of a similar retort for the Matron.

II

On 12 August 1914, Flora Sandes and six other volunteer nurses, under the command of Madame Grouitch, assembled on the platform of Victoria Station to go to War.

Mabel was twenty-six years old, beautiful, American, and married to Slavo Grouitch, Serbian Minister for Foreign Affairs in Nish. Knowing the condition of the nursing services in Serbia, she had come straight to England at the outbreak of war to try and get help. Flora and Mabel had responded to each other immediately. Within minutes Flora was a member of the expedition.

The amateurishness and lack of preparation, the rather giddy femininity of the entire enterprise appealed immensely to Flora. That her elder brothers and the other male relatives thought that they were all completely mad did not worry her in the slightest. They reiterated in loud, bluff voices that it was absurd for a party of unaccompanied women to think they could travel across France at a time like this. Didn't they understand that the trains would all be commandeered? Didn't they realise that France was mobilising for the greatest war in her history? Didn't they know that they would probably need permits to travel from one town to the next?

They would probably all be marooned at some wayside station and forgotten. Worse still, they would all be thrown into gaol and shot as spies. And serve them darn well right too, said her brothers.

Flora ignored them. Besides, she was much too busy collecting all her baggage together to listen to such pessimistic nonsense. This was quite a problem. However, she acquired a portable rubber bath, a sleeping bag, a camp bed, warm clothing, first aid kit, water bottle, sheath knife, revolver, a few thousand cigarettes, and numerous other items she thought necessary for a young woman in foreign parts.

To Flora, that moment at the station was probably the most exciting of her life. Impatient to be off, she had been the first to jump into the railway carriage and the other seven had crowded in after her. Hemmed in by her companions as they crowded at the window, she burrowed amongst them to occupy six grubby inches of London, Brighton and South Coast Railway window.

The platform was crowded with gentlemen in top hats and frock coats, working men in cloth caps or bowlers, wives and sweethearts in hats swirling with ostrich feathers or misty with lace. Children were held up to wave goodbye. Tears were flowing, hands were waving, and people shouting. Flora blinked back the tears from her eyes.

The train begain to slide slowly forward. Within seconds, they had rattled across the bridge over the Thames and were drumming past the drab roofs of suburban London.

Mabel Grouitch sank back in her seat, straightened her hat and adjusted her blouse. Flora brushed her hair back from her forehead and observed her companions. Two were dabbing their eyes. The others were chattering noisily.

Soon they were out in the countryside. The sun streamed through the windows, and the fields, parched and brown from the hottest summer anyone could remember slid quickly past.

Every revolution of the wheels was taking them further and further away from the order, the sanity, and the routine of the life they knew. They were unaware that it would never be the same again: the Victorian virtues, the Edwardian elegance, and the well-defined social standards which had bolstered an Empire, were slipping away like the countryside.

Already, across the Channel, the guns, desultory, remote and menacing, were booming. Along the lanes, long lines of men in khaki, the 'Tommy Atkinses' who had served in the Boer War and on the North-west Frontier, the spit-and-polish professionals of the 'thin red line' tradition, were on the march. They rested in the August heat and occasionally plucked a scarlet poppy from the corn to stick in their caps. They were a small, neat, professional army, highly trained, unique at musketry, with superb morale, and they whistled gaily as they marched towards their inevitable destruction. Their deaths were to be remembered by actions and battles named after small, obscure French towns; a legend which began at Mons and finished four months later with a tombstone above their graves marked, 'Ypres'. The 'old contemptibles' they called themselves, and they died where they fought because it was their duty to do so.

Chattering in their sun-filled carriage, the girls did not know that, the same day, a thousand miles away, the powerful armies of the Austro-Hungarian Empire had crossed the Rivers Drin, Slava and Danube, which marked the border between Austria and Serbia, and launched a ferocious assault upon the small, war-weary and ill-equipped Serbian Army and sent it reeling back under the onslaught. It seemed obvious that this particular theatre of war would be formally resolved by Christmas; that Madame Grouitch and her small party would arrive just in time to observe the armistice proceedings. They crossed the Channel without official interference, and reached Paris without trouble to find it a city of uniforms bathed in golden sunshine. Here they received a surprise.

Mabel paid a courtesy call upon the Serbian Embassy. The Ambassador asked for her help. Many Serbian students studying at the Sorbonne were desperately anxious to get into the war, but the French authorities had neither the time nor inclination to help them. How would it be, he suggested, if they were all issued with one of those charming little Red Cross armbands and joined Mabel's party?

She thought the idea splendid. Had she been asked to transport to Serbia an entire artillery brigade complete with mules, her reply would have been exactly the same.

The next day their train steamed out of the Gare de Lyon. Where it was going nobody knew, probably not even the driver. It was heading hopefully south. The scene on the platform, like that at Victoria, was unforgettable. Friends gathered to wave them goodbye. Champagne flowed, kisses exchanged between the most unlikely people, long and patriotic speeches—most of them drowned—were made, flags were waved and songs sung. It was war in the very best musical comedy tradition. The blood, carnage and misery was to come later.

On this journey Madame Grouitch excelled herself. Whenever they were stuck at a small wayside station, she would at once ask to see the Military Governor. There would be smiles and hand-kissing, motor cars would appear and the young '*Anglaises*' whisked off to the best hotel in town. Next morning the motor-cars would take them back to the station, and after more hand-kissing and a bouquet of flowers for Madame Grouitch, they would continue their journey.

In Italy, however, everything altered. Italy was neutral. The

Italians did not want to be implicated in anybody's war. They were undecided whether to arrest the entire party as spies or detain them because they might infringe Italian neutrality. This went on from station to station all the way to Brindisi at the toe of Italy, but the girls caught the boat for Salonika before anyone could actually make up his mind.

The boat was small and packed. They had to force their way up the gang-plank and on to decks crowded with Greek merchants and citizens, including many Orthodox priests with fine black beards, long black robes and high black hats. Cows were tethered forward, goats amidships, and pigs everywhere. The noise they made was agonising. At last, came a blast on the ship's siren as it shook the boats from its side, and headed out towards the open sea.

Fortunately, the sun beat down from cloudless skies. Clean sea breezes blew away the various smells. The stars shone brightly at night and the sea was calm.

In the early morning, three days later, and almost three weeks after leaving England, the eight girls and thirty students stood in the bows as the cattle-boat steered into the enormous bay leading to Salonika. The sea was as still as a lake, and the city was hidden by the mists which rose from its surface. As the sun climbed higher, the mists turned pink and grey, and slowly cleared to show the houses rising up from the water in a mass of yellow ochres, whites, aquamarines and cyclamen. They saw the crenellated wall of the ancient fort on top of the hill and the dark mountains beyond. Thin, white minarets rose everywhere and the Serbian students, who knew their history, recalled that it had been captured by the Greeks only two years before, and was still a Turkish town.

Smooth as oil, the sea ran up to the long crescent-shaped waterfront, where clusters of rowing boats, small stumpy two-masted schooners and graceful single-masted *caiques* were moored. Facing the town, far away across the bay and dominating it theatrically, stood the high blue shadow of Mount Olympus.

The girls spent only one night in Salonika. The next day they boarded a train which took them, first to the border of Gjevjeli, eighty miles to the north, and then into the mountains beyond.

At dusk, Flora stared out of the carriage window as they jolted through the rugged terrain. When the train whistle blew, it echoed and re-echoed eerily from grey rock faces and deep sombre gorges. Occasionally, she glimpsed a grey-green river, broken by cataracts. Swathes of dark trees covered some of the mountain flanks, but the peaks were mainly naked granite. The moon came out high above them, darting its reflection on the carriage windows. It was a cold alien moon. It made Flora feel very far from home, but it was exciting. That was what mattered.

Chapter Two

MEN WERE all alike, Flora decided. Let their pride be offended in the slightest way and out came their truculence, egoism, pomposity and self-importance. Here she was with Simmo, full of the spirit of helpfulness and dedication, both of them willing to risk their lives in the cause of humanity, and yet, according to this Major Vladimir Georgeovitch, they had, merely by arriving, done him some kind of personal insult.

His initial reaction had been alarming. Were they both mad? he demanded. Didn't they know what was happening in Valjevo, that this was an epidemic of plague proportions, that twenty-one doctors had already died, and that he, Vladimir Georgeovitch, senior surgeon in the Serbian Army, was the only one left? Did they wish to add their bodies to the mass graves; or did they perhaps expect him to bury them personally?

His German was fluent and his temper choleric. He was a short, stocky man with a huge head that looked as if it had been carved out of granite, bristling eyebrows, and a heavy intimidating chin which could not have seen a razor for a week. He wore a grubby white coat, and he looked as if he hadn't slept for a week, either. He was ugly and offensive, Flora decided.

She let him finish. Then, coldly and with dignity, she made her reply.

Almost six months previously she and Miss Simmonds had arrived in Serbia with a small party of nurses led by Madame Mabel Grouitch. Perhaps he had heard of Madame Mabel Grouitch, the wife of the Serbian Minister for Foreign Affairs? They had immediately gone to work in the military hospital at Kragujevac, which had taught them something of the difficulties facing a nurse in a Serbian hospital; they felt, therefore, that they might be of use in another Serbian hospital.

She did not feel it necessary to explain the appalling conditions at Kragujevac. The seven girls had been crowded together in one dark and dirty room, with straw palliasses to sleep on. They had been bitten by bed-bugs and fleas, nauseated by the food, and alarmed to learn that the enemy was only twenty-five miles to the north and liable therefore to break through at any moment. Every day and night, by ox-wagon or railway truck, the wounded, maimed and frost-bitten were delivered to the front door of their hospital. They did not have enough beds for a tenth of them. Their medical stores were wholly inadequate. Yet at the sight of so much human misery and pain they had laboured to bring what comfort they could to the wounded men.

For four months they had endured these conditions. Then, on 3 December 1914, by a brilliant stroke of generalship, General Putnik and his commander in the field General Mishitch, had reversed the situation. In vile weather Mishitch had gathered every available man and driven in at the Austrian centre. They had advanced over terrain the enemy commander had believed impassable, exposed the pitiful inadequacy of the armies of Franz Josef's Austro-Hungarian Empire, and within a few days had driven them back across the frontiers. Belgrade was retaken, and vast quantities of war material and sixty thousand Austrian prisoners were captured. As the fighting along the mountainous frontier regions resolved into stalemate, the wounded at the hospital grew fewer, and there was time to breathe.

It was at this point that Flora and Miss Simmonds conferred together. Miss Simmonds was an American who had known Mabel Grouitch long before she had married a Serbian, and had volunteered as soon as she heard of Mabel's plan.

They were fully aware that conditions in the hospital would not improve. The Serbian hospital authorities had no money to buy bandages, drugs, disinfectants and instruments, and it was Flora who suggested a solution. Why didn't they both go back home, Flora to England, Simmo to the U.S.A., and try to raise money themselves to buy medical stores and equipment?

Simmo thought it a great idea; the hospital director also agreed. They caught a boat to England from Salonika, and Simmo went on to New York.

Prompted by her Red Cross friend in Croydon, Flora wrote a letter to the *Daily Mail*. It was published and she was asked to make a short speech to the members of the Coal Exchange. In three weeks, to her utter astonishment, she had raised over two thousand pounds; Miss Simmonds was equally successful.

Zealously guarding the dozens of packing-cases containing tons of medical supplies, the two girls made the long rail and sea journey back to Serbia.

At this point Flora brought Major Vladimir Georgeovitch back into the story. She told him that when they arrived at Nish, it was Slavo Grouitch who had pointed out that their medical stores were badly needed in Valjevo where a typhus epidemic had broken out. The British Consul, however, had forbidden them to endanger their lives by going there. Moreover, an American doctor friend of Miss Simmonds staying in Nish prophesied that if they went to Valjevo, where the mortality rate was eighty per cent, they would have exactly one month to live.

Undecided, they had returned to the British Consul, and found him reading a letter from Sir Edward Grey, the British Foreign Secretary. It was addressed to all British nurses working in Serbia. It complimented them upon the wonderful work they were doing and urged them to continue; they were to consider any help they could render the Serbs as help to the Allied cause. The British Consul had looked rather sheepish. With support coming from such an unexpected quarter, he said, he had no alternative but to withdraw his previous disapproval, and, if they still wished to go to Valjevo, he wished them the best of luck.

If the Major Georgeovitch didn't want them or their stores, they could turn round and go right back. She was certain that there would be many other hospitals in Serbia which would welcome several tons of medical supplies, plus a trained American surgical nurse, and another nurse, who had made her mark in that well-known British organisation, the Ladies Nursing Yeomanry!

Major Georgeovitch's eyebrows wriggled suspiciously. A surgical nurse! Who'd ever heard of a *female* surgical nurse?

She indicated Miss Simmonds. This lady, she informed him, had been trained in the best hospitals in New York, and worked with some of the finest American surgeons. It was, of course, perfectly true, but as Miss Simmonds spoke hardly a word of German, she was quite unaware of the eulogy.

It had its effect upon Major Georgeovitch, however. From the moment Flora had started to talk, his attitude changed. Cases of medical supplies? And a surgical nurse? There were literally hundreds of patients in this hospital and in the town with gangrenous limbs needing immediate surgery. He turned to them and threw wide his arms. Could they blame him for trying to send them away? He was endeavouring to save their lives. Twenty-one doctors had already died. Another doctor, an American, was at this very moment dying in the Balkan Hotel. However, if they were mad enough to stay after all he had told them, he would not stop them. Of course they wanted to stay, Flora said sharply. They were nurses, their duty was to help the sick. Could he arrange to have all the cases of medical supplies brought to the hospital from the station?

The Major nodded slowly. Yes, that could be done. What had they got? Bandages, ether, medicines, disinfectants, surgical instruments; Flora went through the list, and she watched Major Georgeovitch repeat each item in turn as if he was intoning a passage from the Koran. This was absolutely miraculous! Why hadn't they told him all this before?

They had, said Flora severely, but he hadn't listened.

He apologised. They must think him boorish, ungrateful, rude and impossible. But now he would try and make amends. He smiled. First they must get rooms in the hotel. He would send an orderly to show them the way and afterwards they would discuss their work.

The hospital orderly, a pale thin youth, led the way through the streets. Flora had already decided that Valjevo was a dreary little town. The buildings were small, single-storey and dingy, and only a few streets were cobbled. The snow-covered mountains lacked grandeur. They had not gone more than thirty yards from the front door when they saw an ox-cart creaking slowly towards them. She shuddered as she realised it was full of corpses on their way to the mass grave.

Halfway down the street, in a recess in the walls roughly covered with canvas, twenty soldiers were gathered. Most of them were lying motionless, wrapped in their ground-sheets. One, with a blanket round his shoulders, was poking at the embers of a fire with a stick and roasting half a dozen corn-cobs. He did not look up as they passed.

The hotel front was flat, with crumbling plaster walls, and a sign above the door said in faded black letters, 'Balkan Hotel'. The entrance was gloomy, the stone-flagged floor unwashed. The proprietor at the desk inside was old and shrivelled. He wore a black fur cap and a drooping moustache. His skin was sallow, his eyes bloodshot and his breath reeked of brandy. He spoke bad German but listened to their request.

'A room?' Yes, that could be managed, although many of them were filled with people dying of typhus. An American doctor? Yes, there was one dying upstairs. There was no pity in his voice, and no surprise. Too many had died.

He trod very slowly up the stairs and opened a creaking door on the first floor. Inside the small room were two beds, two chairs, and a marble-topped wash-stand with a jug and a bowl upon it. It was uncarpeted and comfortless. In one bed lay an emaciated man with staring eyes who groaned weakly for water when they went in. Miss Simmonds hurried to the wash-stand, filled a glass from the jug, gently lifted his head and helped him to sip. Then she took a thermometer from her bag, pushed it into his mouth and felt his pulse.

Flora's attention was held by the other bed. On it was a coffin made of freshly-sawn pine planks. The proprietor caught her glance, and mistook it for admiration. Yes, he said blandly, he had wanted to make the poor fellow's end a little easier. There were few coffins in Valjevo. This one had been hard to get. But for an American, so far from home, it was but a small service. Flora agreed tartly that it was most thoughtful.

Miss Simmonds went over to the window to examine her thermometer. She glanced at the coffin and said it must be removed at once. She had never seen anything quite so disgusting in all her life. Flora did not feel it necessary to translate this last remark to the old man. The doctor was obviously through the worst, Miss Simmonds continued. He needed good nursing and feeding, that was all. But they could certainly do with a lot of hot water and fresh linen to clean the place up.

Flora translated to the old man who nodded but seemed a little hurt when she went on to mention the coffin. He could not believe that they wanted it removed. He eyed it thoughtfully for a few seconds. He would get it taken out, he told her, but would keep it handy 'just in case'. He gave her another meaningful look. After he went out, Miss Simmonds grinned. 'A little more encouragement and he would have asked you to try it for size,' she said.

Flora watched her re-arranging the sick man's sheets. Her hair was caught up in a plain bun at the back of her neck, she wore a

Family group outside Marlsford Rectory. Flora (extreme right) is aged sixteen. Back row: the Reverend Mr. Sandes and his wife. The others are brothers, a sister and cousins

Flora, holding rear end of a stretcher during an exercise with the Ladies' Nursing Yeomanry

Serbian wounded being brought down from the front line by mule litter

Two privates of the 4th Company on parade with newly issued British boots and French rifles

white blouse and a dark skirt, no jewellery of any sort, and her hands were broad and practical with square, neatly-trimmed fingernails.

She was not pretty, but she was a warm, generous, energetic person. Despite her placid exterior, Flora knew that she burned with a fierce New England puritanism, which had little to do with religion. She was a professional humanitarian and an instinctive suffragette. She believed that every human being had a fundamental right to food, shelter and medical aid. She had no sympathy for lady-of-the-manor charity. She knew one had to be wholly committed. She hated war, but she knew that it created tragic opportunities for her craft.

She was more practical than Flora, who was always burning to fight for some lost cause and was luckily blessed with a vast and incurable optimism. It was not the 'God will provide' optimism of the great saints and the inspired missionaries, but that of the naturally courageous and the sublimely innocent.

Together they made a formidable combination. Even Major Georgeovitch quickly realised this. That evening when they returned to the hospital he took them on a conducted tour. Soldiers, wounded, sick or dying of typhus, lay everywhere: in every ward, in every corridor, on the cold floor, in their muddy, blood-stained uniforms, they were waiting, usually for death.

Next morning the convalescent American doctor told the girls that they must leave at once. The outbreak had started with the Austrian prisoners. It had quickly reached plague proportions, and nothing could check it. There were lice everywhere. They could not stay in Valjevo without being infected.

Flora protested that she had heard if you smeared paraffin all over your body and along the seams of your clothing you had a fair chance of discouraging the bugs.

They would not succeed, he said. They would incubate the disease for about twelve to fourteen days, then they would have a headache and not be able to sleep. Their temperatures would rise to between 103 and 105 degrees. Their tongues would become coated with a white fur which would gradually turn brown. They would feel intensely thirsty and within days mud-coloured spots would appear on their skins. They would then fall into a coma, so closely resembling death that they might quite possibly be buried alive. About the fourteenth day the crisis would come;

their temperatures would plummet to sub-normal, and they would certainly die. Their bodies would be thrown into the death-cart which went around the streets two or three times a day, and they would be buried in a mass grave. Nothing would mark the spot where they were buried, and neither their family nor friends would ever hear of them again.

It was a grave warning and they discussed it until late into the night. Not that there was really any doubt about what course to take. They were committed: to Vladimir Georgeovitch as much as anyone. Perhaps if they hadn't been to the hospital and offered their services they might have considered the doctor's warning more seriously.

They saw him off on the train back to Nish a few days later. He still entreated them to come back with him. Flora told him it was too late; for better or worse they were staying in Valjevo.

That first morning when they reported to the Major, he explained what he wanted them to do. Miss Simmonds had told him that she was a qualified surgical nurse. Could the two of them take over the operating-theatre? There were hundreds of men in the hospital needing surgical attention: gangrenous limbs were a common result of typhus.

Miss Simmonds looked Flora hard in the eyes and said they would do their best. But was there an operating-theatre? He led them through the corridors and pushed open the door of a large empty room. It was filthy. It contained one wooden operating-table and one dilapidated bed. The Major explained that he had always intended to use it but had never had the time.

While they were inspecting the theatre they became aware of two Serbian faces in the doorway. Major Georgeovitch introduced them. Bozidar and Milan were to act as orderlies. Bozidar was six feet three in height, dark, hairy, amiable and strong as an ox. Milan was short, dark and eager; he spoke excellent German. When the Major left, Flora asked Milan if there were many soldiers with gangrenous wounds.

With a beaming smile, he told her that he knew of hundreds, mostly with gangrenous feet. They would have to be cut off, would they not? The prospect seemed to please him.

Flora felt her stomach heave. She translated his remarks to Simmo who eyed her severely and told her that it would mean just what he said.

She took a deep breath and observed that she would be all right as long as there was a bucket handy. As an afterthought, she added, 'Have you ever cut off anybody's foot before?'

'No, but there's always a first time,' said Miss Simmonds primly. 'Thank goodness we've got ether and proper equipment.'

Before Flora left England she had been presented with a case of surgical instruments. At the time she had thought they would make a marvellous present for some overworked Serbian surgeon. She had never dreamt that she might be helping to use them *herself*!

Simmo tried to cheer her up. She had assisted with hundreds of operations, she said, and Flora could act as anaesthetist. She would have the job of soaking the pad in ether and holding it over the patient's nose and mouth.

'If it gets too bad I'll probably take a whiff myself,' said Flora unhappily.

Simmo surveyed the operating-theatre with distaste. 'First of all we must get this place scrubbed out,' she said. 'Tell our two tame gorillas that we need boiling water, brooms, brushes, everything!'

By midday the room had been scrubbed out and disinfected. They had found an old sterilizer under the bed; and the surgical instruments were now boiling away gently inside it.

Bozidar carried the first patient in his arms like a baby and laid him gently on the table. The young soldier wore a stained and muddy uniform. His face was pale, rough with stubble, and his left foot was swathed in a mass of dirty rags. Even so he managed a weak smile.

Simmo gently cut the rags away. They fell back to reveal a blackened, shrivelled foot. He had been hit in the ankle by a piece of shrapnel, and gangrene was obviously creeping up his leg. The smell, rather than the sight, made Flora feel sick.

'You can see for yourself,' Simmo said gravely, 'we must either amputate or this man will eventually die. The choice is as simple as that.'

Flora explained it in German to Milan who translated it into Serbian.

'The soldier says he quite understands,' reported Milan cheerfully, 'will you please cut it off as quickly as possible?'

Flora felt that there was something incongruous in this reply.

'Does he know we're going to give him chloroform?' she asked.

As she spoke she looked down at the young soldier and saw that his eyes were fixed upon a point just behind her right shoulder. She turned to see what he was staring at. A packet of cigarettes lay on a shelf where she had placed them ten minutes earlier.

She turned back to Milan. 'Tell him,' she said, 'that if he behaves well he can have the whole packet.'

Milan translated. Flora saw a far-away look come into the soldier's eyes. Then he smiled and said something in Serbian. 'He answer,' said Milan, 'that he would rather have the cigarettes than the chloroform.'

'You tell him,' she said severely, 'that it is not a *choice*! He's getting the chloroform anyway.'

'Having trouble?' asked Miss Simmonds.

'Just a little misunderstanding,' she soaked the pad of gauze in ether and held it gently over the soldier's nose and mouth.

'Tell him to breathe in deeply,' she ordered Milan.

His eyes slowly closed. She lifted the pad away so that it was about half an inch from his face, ready to re-apply it should he stir.

Simmo made the first deep incision with the scalpel. Flora looked away but forced her eyes back again. The noise of the bone-saw made her want to retch, but she clenched her teeth.

In five minutes the foot was off and the stump had been sutured and bandaged.

Flora felt the room getting hotter. She excused herself and went outside to the bucket. She leaned against the wall of the corridor. It was cool and reassuring. Somehow she had to summon up enough courage to go back inside. Then she heard a male voice speaking gentle, fluent German. She looked down. On the other side of the narrow corridor was a window recess. His head pillowed on a haversack, lay a young soldier in a shabby Austrian overcoat, his legs covered by a dirty blanket. He was very young, slight and fair. His eyes were blue. He was asking if he could help.

Flora wiped her mouth with the back of her hand and took a deep breath.

'Help me? In your condition? What's the matter with you?'

He said that he had had typhus but was all right now.

'You're Austrian?' she asked. He nodded.

'A prisoner of war?' Another nod.

'What are you doing here?'

He smiled faintly. 'There are a lot of us here. They say we brought the typhus. In the room I was in I could not stand the smell and the noise. I decided it would be better to die alone out here.'

'And you didn't die?'

'No.'

'Funny place to choose,' she laughed. 'Do they feed you?'

'Yes, I have the same food as the others.'

She fished a cigarette out of her pocket and offered him a match. His face brightened as he sucked at the cigarette and blew out the smoke.

'Thank you,' he said. 'You speak good German. Are you French?'

'English.'

'You are the first English I ever met,' he said.

'We'll choose a better place next time,' said Flora.

Back in the operating-theatre the young Serbian soldier was sitting up grinning. He was also smoking a cigarette and clutched the packet from the shelf. He offered her one and said something in Serbian to Milan, who lit her cigarette and translated, 'He asks, do you feel all right now?'

She laughed. The whole thing should have been so tragic. A young man had lost his foot and would be a cripple for the rest of his life, but he could still joke about her squeamishness. Perhaps things would not be so bad after all.

For the next few days they operated from eight in the morning until seven at night.

She also began to operate herself. Miss Simmonds needed a rest from time to time and during every operation instructed Flora in the art of surgery. 'Now the difference between a Syme's amputation and Pirogoff's is that the "tendo Achilles" is divided from the posterior,' she would say. Surgery for beginners, Flora called it. Practically all the amputations they did were on feet, and there was no lack of patients. Gradually Flora's nervousness disappeared.

They also found a new and useful assistant in the Austrian prisoner, Willy. Flora never quite understood why she felt sorry for him. Possibly it was his youth or his disarming manner. She pointed out to Simmo that there was absolutely no point in his sleeping in the draughty corridor when the operating-theatre was usually empty between eight at night and six in the morning, so she told him he could sleep on the dilapidated bed. He moved in gratefully. As his convalescence progressed, he ran errands and kept the place clean. Soon he began to help with the operations, as anaesthetist.

In Valjevo death struck at the rate of two hundred a day, and it soon became clear that the epidemic could not be confined to the town alone. Within weeks it had spread throughout Serbia. More than a hundred thousand people—far more than were killed or wounded in the fighting—died of the disease. And one third of the doctors also died. When the plague finally burnt itself out less than a hundred were left in the whole country.

Once a day they could all relax. This was after eight o'clock in the evening when all the staff collected for dinner. The dining-room was long and bare. A well-scrubbed wooden table ran down the centre, with high-backed chairs lining each side. On the white-washed wall behind each chair, hung a small black-framed notice which briefly commemorated the death by typhus of the previous occupant.

Yet there was always a cheerful atmosphere in the dining-room. Everyone was determined to be gay. Mention of the word 'typhus' was taboo, so they talked of peace, of summer, of holidays in the south, of strange towns and romantic adventures. There were twelve senior staff, fourteen with Flora and Miss Simmonds. Each night they joked and laughed and sang. Even Vladimir sang solos in a melodious tenor voice, and the two women joined in the choruses. They raised their glasses in endless toasts. Everyone got a little drunk. 'Don't go to bed,' a voice would call, when anyone made a move. 'Stay up tonight! Stay up! You know nothing of tomorrow! Why go to bed?'

Each night the group grew smaller. One by one they fell sick. Every evening Flora and Miss Simmonds would walk in to dinner and find that the chair opposite to them or next to them was empty.

At the end of their second week in the hospital the group around the drinking table was down to six. At the end of the third week, three were left: the Major, Flora and Miss Simmonds. It was now clear that the epidemic had won.

Only the Major seemed impervious to it all. 'Bugs have been biting me since childhood,' he told them cheerfully. 'I probably kill off hundreds.' The only thing that could save them was the spring, he went on. Typhus was a winter disease. When the spring came and the sun shone, it would disappear. But would any of them be left alive to see that moment when it arrived?

So the days passed. Flora did not count them. You were supposed to have twenty-eight days' grace from the moment you were infected, but who knew when you were infected? And they were far too busy to count.

They knew it might happen to either of them at any moment. Both knew it and avoided thinking about it. When at half-past six one morning Flora went into her friend's room at the Balkan Hotel to find out what was delaying her, and discovered that she was still in bed, the shock was not as great as it might have been. Simmo's face was flushed, her breathing heavy. She lay in a semi-coma. Flora needed no expert opinion; she had seen too many others at the hospital. This was typhus.

Georgeovitch arrived within half an hour. He examined her and shook his head grimly. 'May God help her. He is the only one who can.'

He turned to Flora. 'How about you?' he asked. Flora said she was all right. Her feelings were numbed. It was difficult to understand that Simmo was very sick and had about one chance in five of recovering. Could she carry on with the work at the operating theatre? he demanded. Flora nodded. She could cope, with Willy's assistance, but someone would have to nurse Simmo. She could look after her in the evening and at night, but what about the rest of the time?

The Major nodded thoughtfully. He would arrange to have an orderly permanently by her side.

Very depressed, she set off for the hospital. Usually she enjoyed the short walk: but that morning nothing could help her. Poor old Simmo! In spite of all the warnings, both of them had believed—stupidly perhaps—in their own personal immortality. Now reality had caught up with them.

Early that afternoon Milan came rushing excitedly into the theatre. A visitor had arrived, someone of great importance. Colonel Sondermayor, the Director of Medical Services, had come upon a visit of inspection. What should he do?

'Oh, for heaven's sake, go away,' said Flora testily. As if they hadn't enough trouble without people coming around inspecting. The man must be mad!

A soldier with a gangrenous foot was stretched out upon the operating-table. Willy had just administered ether, and Flora had the knife in her hand, ready for the first incision.

A man strode in with all the confidence of high rank and personal grandeur. He was middle-aged and wore the smart, high-collared uniform of a staff officer. His boots were highly polished, his epaulettes gleamed with gold, and his cropped head bristled like a clothes brush. This was clearly Colonel Sondermayor and he looked very formidable.

His eyes were dark and deep-set. Flora always insisted they started an inch forward when they saw an Austrian prisoner of war holding a chloroform pad over the face of a Serbian soldier, and a strange woman with an amputating knife poised above his foot. He gulped and seemed to have some difficulty in moving his lips. Then he said in German, in a very odd voice, 'Who is the surgeon here?'

Flora put down her instrument and made an amateurish attempt to stand to attention.

'I am, sir,' she said meekly. There was a moment of silence. The Director's face did not alter. He merely looked up at the ceiling. Then, quite deliberately, he raised his right hand and crossed himself three times.

'Carry on,' he said, 'do the best you can.' He saluted, turned on his heel and went out.

Her position as senior surgeon at Valjevo lasted precisely forty-eight hours. After that everything became blurred. She remembered going to bed that night, then waking and feeling her head throbbing, and her body on fire. She had no sense of fear. She knew she had typhus.

She did not know until much later that Willy, alarmed at not seeing her at the hospital, had run all the way to the hotel and found her in a raving delirium; or that he had run all the way back to fetch Major Georgeovitch and that both of them had doubled back to the hotel.

The Major watched Willy bathe her forehead and arrange the pillow under her head. There were tears on Willy's cheeks. He had never forgotten the way she had befriended him. Now she was sick and he intended to nurse her. He asked the Major's permission, and it was willingly given.

For the next three weeks Willy hardly ever left her bedroom. He slept at the foot of her bed and was up at the slightest murmur or movement.

For Flora it was a lost three weeks. Vaguely she remembered swimming into consciousness out of immense swirling clouds, hearing Willy's voice comfort her in its soft Tyrolean accent; or screaming in her nightmares and waking to find herself clutching his hand.

It was Major Georgeovitch who told her about her 'lost' three weeks. He also told her that Willy had washed her, and changed her nightclothes, given her bed-pans and raced backwards and forwards to the hospital kitchen to get soup and other food.

During the night of the crisis Willy had sat beside her bed, taking her temperature every few minutes and holding her hands.

Several times during her illness her pulse had apparently stopped altogether. Her heart had become inaudible; apparently she ceased to breathe.

Had she obeyed the normal rules of typhus, said the Major sternly, but with a slight smile, she would certainly not be lying in this bed now. She would be dead. She never had been very good at obeying rules, he could see that. He patted her arm and said that both she and Miss Simmonds should be up and about quite shortly. Obviously God had decided it was worth keeping them both alive for other duties.

So the plague which devastated Serbia in the winter of 1915 burned itself out.

Spring brought a renewal of life, and, in the quiet corners of gardens where the sun reached, green shoots suddenly sprouted from the brown earth. Almost overnight white blossom appeared on the black branches of the plum and cherry trees. The snow melted away on the lower slopes, and the grass, at first brown and shrivelled, was green and fresh within hours. The scent of lilac and basil floated through the windows. Stony mountain streams became full of bright chattering torrents racing down to join the deep green rivers of the valley, and by some feat of bargaining Willy suddenly produced fresh brown trout for supper. The typhus lice, feeling the spring sunshine, grew old and tired and disappeared.

It was almost two months before Flora and Simmo were well enough to return to the hospital. They found many changes. It was May. The sun shone from a clear blue sky and relief doctors had arrived. The death-carts no longer made daily excursions to the mass graves at the edge of the town. No new typhus cases were reported.

The war was static too. The Serbs were holding their lines in the north. Along the western front trench warfare had settled down into its normal pattern of bloody attrition, but here all was quiet. The Serbs knew, however, that the Bulgars were massing across the frontier, and they were anxious to attack before they were ready. Britain and France insisted that they should do no such thing. Both Allies foolishly believed that somehow Bulgaria could be induced to fight against Germany in defence of Serbia, and nothing could dissuade them.

Late in August Major Georgeovitch called Flora and Simmo into his office. The summer was almost over, and it was unlikely that any enemy offensive would be mounted. Neither was fully recovered, so he gave them three months' leave of absence. This was an order. Did they understand?

They understood and were grateful. They found it difficult to say goodbye to all the friends they had made, especially to Willy and the Major himself to whom they had become very attached.

The last thing Flora saw as the train drew out from Valjevo station was Willy and the Major waving farewell.

'We'll be back,' she screamed above the noise of the engine, 'we shan't be long!'

She did not realise then that the war rarely allowed you to make your own decisions. War picked you up and whisked you away, and if it didn't manage to kill you with a bullet or a bomb it tried to destroy you in a variety of other ways.

She would be back—yes, but not in the way she expected. The Major had been wrong. The enemy *could* mount an autumn offensive and did. It was a campaign which was to change the history of Serbia and alter Flora's life for ever.

Chapter Three

I

THE BRITISH CONSUL at Monastir was a tall, thin young man with an engaging manner: his clothes were well-cut, his voice pleasantly modulated, and his education had obviously been thorough and expensive.

These facts made no impression whatsoever upon the four girls who confronted him. Up against Flora Sandes, in her tailored khaki breeches and jacket, backed by Lady Muriel Herbert, in her chamois-leather coat and skirt, with a red silk scarf tied carelessly around her throat, Elia Linden, in her French nurse's uniform complete with flowing white cloak and blue tulle veil, and Dolly Miles, practical and aggressive in her white overalls and three sweaters unevenly buttoned underneath, the Consul knew he was trapped. He was confronted by four militant suffragettes indoctrinated not only with the belief that women were always as good as men, but often a great deal better. An experience for which the Foreign Office had not prepared him.

He told Flora that Valjevo, which she was trying to reach, had been overrun by the enemy long before; he explained that not forty miles from this very town the 1st Serbian Army was clinging tenaciously to defences around the Baboona Pass; he warned that if they took the road northwards they would all be raped and have their throats cut by the bands of Bulgar *comitjades*. The girls remained quite unperturbed.

Monastir, capital of Macedonia, had been liberated by the Serbians only two years earlier, and renamed Bitola, but after four hundred years of Turkish rule it was still predominantly a Turkish town, inhabited by a mixed population of Bulgars, Macedonians and Turks, who eye the girls with hostility.

The town stood at the apex of a triangular-shaped valley in the mountains. On each side of the triangle, rose mountains six thousand feet high, barren and oppressive, but southwards the valley was fertile: it widened out into the rolling northern plains of Greece; the fields grew maize and wheat and supplied pasture to herds of cattle and goats. It had been used as a pathway into Europe by conquerors since pre-Roman times. Alexander had marched along it, and his route was soon to become a battlefield again.

As in the days of Turkish ownership, it was a town of character and grace, of consulates and embassies, of small green squares where flimsy, ornamental bridges crossed little streams, and uninspired statues made convenient perches for pigeons. Everywhere, against the background of mountains and foreground of huddled buildings and thick-tiled roofs, rose minarets of white or grey stones. Symmetrical and lovely, they admonished the infidel and proclaimed the Muslim faith to the true believer.

At that moment Flora did not care twopence for any true believer. She was angry. A few weeks she had been involved in the war, perhaps not doing anything terribly important, but at least doing *something*; now she was inactive. It was most infuriating, and this silly young British Consul wasn't helping.

As soon as she reached England with Miss Simmonds and saw her off on a boat for America, she realised that things at home had changed drastically. This was not going to be like those other 'little' wars fought in Mashonaland and against the Fuzzy-wuzzies and along the ramparts of the Empire. Now, when you opened a newspaper, instead of glorious victories and stirring retreats, you saw scores of men's names in tiny black print in what they called casualty lists. Something had gone dreadfully wrong.

She discovered that few people knew anything at all about Serbia, and didn't want to know anything about it, either; they had troubles enough of their own. As far as they were concerned it was a silly little war and she had no right to waste time over it. They had heard of Salonika, yes. After all British and French soldiers, under an agreement with Venizelos, the Greek Prime Minister, had just been evacuated there from Gallipoli.

The news that the Bulgars had treacherously invaded Serbia, to coincide with a large-scale attack by German and Austro-Hungarian forces, did little to change public opinion. But as soon as Flora heard about it, she set about returning to Serbia as quickly as possible, where she was needed.

She sent a cable to Simmo telling her that they would link up again as soon as she managed to get back to Serbia, and set off to catch a boat at Marseilles. On October 20 she boarded the Messagerie Maritime steamer *Mossoul* and almost at once joined up with Lady Muriel Herbert, Elia Linden and Dolly Miles, who were all going out to rejoin medical units in Serbia.

They arrived at Salonika on November 3 and found the town buzzing like a disturbed bee-hive. One thing was plain. The northern and eastern territories of Serbia had been completely overrun. The railway line running northwards through Nish to Belgrade had been cut. Three French divisions had already gone up the line to try and link up with the Serbians, and the 10th British Division, just disembarked from Gallipoli, was moving northwards to reinforce them.

It soon became clear that the only hope Flora had of reaching Valjevo was to catch the train which ran westwards from Salonika along the northern boundary of Greece and then turned up into Macedonia and finished at Monastir, the old Turkish capital.

The other three girls decided to try their luck with her. After an uncomfortable night on the train, they arrived in the British Consul's office and found him unco-operative. They quickly settled that. Eventually it was the Consul, Mr Greig, who capitulated.

That afternoon, he informed them, he was driving up the main road to Prilep, the next town on the way north. It was about twenty-five miles from Monastir. An armed escort was accompanying him but, if they cared to take the risk, they could come too and find out what was really happening.

The chauffeur-driven limousine in which they travelled was a venerable and highly-polished vehicle, made by coach-builders who had identified the new motor age with their own crafts of tooled leather and hand-moulded metal, and it would not have disgraced a royal procession. The girls sat up in the high back seat, Mr Greig next to his chauffeur, immaculately dressed in a buttoned overcoat, peaked cap and gauntlets.

The road northwards was bad. It was narrow, twisting and potholed and the wheels raised great clouds of dust. Flora realised that it was not bravery but elementary common-sense which had prompted Mr Greig to arrange for the lorry-load of soldiers to drive behind them. Twice they needed the soldiers' help when the car stuck in the mud.

Prilep was a smaller edition of Monastir, but shabbier and more agitated. It was full of unshaven Turks in baggy trousers and scarlet fezzes, Macedonians and Bulgars in fur hats and clothes of homespun wool, and detachments of muddy, exhausted-looking Serbian soldiers.

At the Serbian Military Hospital they talked to the Director of Medical Services, who was courteous but very worried. He told them anxiously that, unless help in the shape of men and arms from the French and British arrived very shortly, the Serbs would be forced to retreat. The 1st Army was clinging to the heights around the Baboona Pass some twenty miles away. They were short of ammunition, guns, food, medical supplies, everything in fact, and they were facing fresh armies of Austro-Hungarians, Germans and Bulgars immeasurably superior in numbers and armament. If only they could receive help, they would hold. Could Mr Greig prophesy when help might come?

Mr Greig could not. Flora, who had seen the chaos back in Salonika, made no comment. In terms of rail transport she knew it was impossible to move an army up here, even if such an army existed in Salonika. More than that, the Allies were only in Greece upon the slenderest of pretexts: a military pact which Serbia had made with Greece some years before, and through the good graces of Venizelos, the pro-Allied Greek Prime Minister.

As there was little comfort in these thoughts, Flora kept her mouth shut. She did, however, ask if she could stay and help in the hospital at Prilep. She had brought the most essential part of her baggage with her and, if necessary, perhaps Mr Greig would not object to sending up the rest?

The Director was delighted, and Mr Greig at last smiled. If he could not summon up a regiment of artillery, at least he had provided one volunteer British nurse. The other three girls decided to return to Salonika and join one of the medical units there.

Flora spent that night in the only hotel in Prilep, a small dingy place called 'La Nouvelle Serbia'. The Director had lent an elderly male orderly to help her settle in, and Flora gave him the job of scrubbing out her room. She then set up her camp bed and moved in. The patrons in the hotel below were unshaven, ill-dressed and surly, so she carefully examined the lock on her door. Supported by the back of a chair wedged upwards on two legs, it would provide a reasonable first line of defence.

That night, scribbling in her diary by candlelight, her loaded revolver on the floor beside her, she wrote: 'Monday, 8th, 8.30 p.m. I am sitting up in bed in my sleeping-bag writing this in a very small room. The room contains besides my camp bed, a rickety chair and a small table with my little rubber basin, a cracked mirror and my faithful tea-basket. . . . The view from my window is not calculated to inspire confidence either. It looks on to a stableyard full of pigs, donkeys and the most villainous-looking Turks squatting about at their supper. These, I tell myself, are the ones who will come in and cut my throat if Prilep is taken tonight, as I don't think any responsible person in the town knows I am here. However, if I live through the night things will probably look more cheery in the morning.'

Down below she could hear the locals, flushed with plum brandy and wine, singing loud and repetitive choruses, but she was so tired that eventually she blew out her candle and went to sleep.

About midnight she awoke to the sound of heavy boots on the stairs and her door-handle rattling violently. She sat up and reached for her revolver. This was the sort of occasion her maiden aunts had warned her about. The tattoo upon the door panels continued, and a thick masculine voice made threatening noises. Flora thumbed off the safety-catch of her revolver and said in a voice which she hoped was firm and clear, 'Go away!'

This only produced more blows and an incoherent babble of threats.

'Go away,' said Flora, 'I've got a gun!'

She heard more noise on the stairs. It was the hotel proprietor. He joined in the argument. She guessed he was telling the intruder that the room was occupied by a young lady of impeccable virtue. From the reply she gathered, however, that the man was not the slightest bit interested in her impeccable virtue, he was concerned only with the fact that she had stolen his room!

In a noble surge of Balkan politeness, the hotel proprietor had let the room twice. However, he seemed to be winning the argument, so Flora thumbed back the safety catch again and snuggled down into her sleeping-bag.

In the middle of the night she was wakened a second time by more noise on the stairs. This time it seemed it was the friends of the man whose room she was occupying: they had come to share it with him. They rattled the doorknob and banged on the panels. As the hotel proprietor was obviously fast asleep and not on hand to defend her, she thought of firing a bullet through the door above their heads. She reflected firstly, however, that they might fire back, and, secondly, the townspeople might decide that the enemy had really arrived and a fierce battle break out. Moreover, the hotel was so old and dilapidated that even a small explosion might bring it down.

The new intruders were obviously very drunk. Soon the rattles grew feebler, the entreaties dwindled; finally only snores and occasional grunts filtered under the door. Flora went back to sleep.

Next morning she told the Medical Director of her disturbed night. Something must de done, he said, and he took her round to meet Prilep's Chief of Police, a fat, dark, rosy-cheeked little man, who laughed out loud at her story. Flora glared at him angrily.

Seeing her face, he converted his laughter into coughs of disapproval and said he knew exactly the place for her. A hundred yards from the gate of the hospital, he knocked on the front door of a neat little house. The widow who owned it made a great fuss of Flora and said she would be delighted to look after her. She showed her to a clean well-furnished room, and for the rest of her stay in Prilep Flora's nights were quiet and unadventurous.

The idea of joining an ambulance unit close to the fighting line itself was not really her scheme at all. Many of the wounded soldiers in the hospital came from the 2nd Regiment, part of the 1st Army which was holding the Baboona Pass. They said that as the 1st Army was the best in all Serbia, and the 2nd Regiment the best in that Army and possessed two field ambulance units, why didn't she join one of them? Women could serve in ambulance units. They even served in the army, mainly in non-combatant jobs: as ammunition carriers and as cooks, and they weren't above using a rifle if need be.

The idea began to take shape in her mind. At any moment, she expected to see Mr Greig, or a messenger of his, coming to say that, as a non-combatant British subject, she had no right at all to be in such a dangerous area, and that as he was responsible for her safety, she would have to return to Salonika. She did not know what rights she possessed in such an emergency, but if she was miles away he would have a devil of a job even to find her, and if she managed to conceal herself in a field ambulance unit, he probably wouldn't be able to find her at all.

She approached the Medical Director. Could he help her? He thought the idea was excellent. When he next visited Monastir he would make a formal request to the military authorities.

Several days later he handed her a buff-coloured envelope. It contained a military authorization for Flora Sandes to join the field ambulance unit of the 2nd Regiment as soon as practicable.

If she wanted to leave that same afternoon, he continued, the Chief of Police could arrange transport. This was a carriage, a four-wheeled affair with a broken hood, bent springs and upholstery which oozed horsehair stuffing, and might have been dragged from some rubbish dump. Its driver was a frail old man in a woollen homespun suit and a sheepskin cap. His two skinny horses looked as if they would scarcely manage to pull the carriage over the first hill. The Chief of Police, however, laughed heartily, smacked the horses' rumps, said they were good nags, and that, after all, the fighting was only ten or fifteen miles away and they should have no difficulty. Besides, the Medical Director was allowing her old orderly to go along in case of any difficulty.

They set off just after lunch, Flora with her two aged companions. They had not gone more than two miles out of the town along a road, as bumpy, narrow and twisting as the one between Prilep and Monastir, when a strap of the harness broke. The old driver got out, grumbling, and repaired it with a piece of string. He was obviously used to it.

They bounced and rattled along for another few miles and turned along a narrow track winding round the side of a mountain. The edge of the road fell away steeply to a river which boiled and hissed over jagged rocks. Beyond the river the mountain rose steeply again, thickly wooded and dark. The wheels skidded and slithered perilously on the loose gravel, and Flora decided that the river would probably get her if the Bulgarians didn't.

They skidded down the mountainside, crossed a stream by a flimsy bridge, and the old horses slowly began the long haul up another mountainside. She got out and walked, making the old orderly do the same.

Five miles farther on the harness again broke, and once more the driver did running repairs with his piece of string. It was growing dark now, and from the top of the next mountain she saw faint flashes lighting the sky and heard the rumble of artillery fire. She looked at the orderly who pulled a wry face, and agreed they were the flashes of the Bulgar batteries. At first she felt a bit frightened.

Then she thought over the situation and chuckled aloud. It really was too absurd. Here she was, driving off to war in an old carriage tied up with bits of string, accompanied by two flimsy gentlemen who should have been pensioned off years ago.

A little later the driver stopped the carriage and held a short conference with the old orderly. He wanted to turn back. She said no. They would drive on for another twenty minutes and, if they hadn't found anybody by then, they would hold a second conference. Reluctantly the driver shook up the horses and the carriage creaked onwards. On the rocky outcrops in the road, the horses' hooves echoed loudly and occasionally struck little sparks in the darkness. The wind stirred uneasily in the trees and once, far away, she heard what sounded like the howl of a dog. The old orderly said it was a wolf. There were lots in these mountains, he said.

The twenty minutes were almost up when, rounding a bend, they saw a camp fire burning under some rocks at the side of the road. She heard two rifle bolts click back and snap home as bullets went up into their breeches. A voice challenged loudly in Serbian. They had found the Field Ambulance of the 2nd Regiment of the 1st Army.

II

The Field Ambulance stood in a small valley surrounded by low hills: one large tent with half a dozen small bivouac tents clustered around it. Beyond the low hills rose the mountains, their craggy shoulders already powdered with the first autumn snow. Crowded within the valley was the narrow dusty road, a short expanse of grass, and a small stream that ran bubbling over white stones. Rising upwards on either side, stretched a thick screen of spruce trees which ended halfway up the hillside.

It was rather like a picturesque English valley. The previous night, at Flora's insistence, they had pitched her tent a few yards away from the others and heaped fresh straw inside it. She slept well. She was awakened by a girl called Maria, who looked about sixteen years old, and who scolded her because she had insisted upon placing her tent away from the others. When Flora smiled, Maria said sternly that she must remember that this part of the mountains was full of Bulgar *comitjades* who might creep in and slit her throat.

Maria was pretty even though her Serbian soldier's uniform of rough brown-grey homespun tweed fitted badly in places. Her skin was tanned, her black hair cut in a severe fringe across her forehead, and she had dark eyes under her arched eyebrows. She was a country girl who had joined the Field Ambulance after her village had been destroyed by enemy shelling. What had happened to her mother and father, brothers and sisters she did not know.

When Flora walked across to the stream to wash, Maria followed her. The water was icy. Flora soaped her hands and face, and then rinsed away the suds. When she had finished, her hands and face were glowing, and she pushed the soap and towel into the hands of Maria, who smiled with pleasure but sniffed the soap cautiously before she bent to wash. Flora looked at her as she splashed around. She was so young and pretty, she should really have been helping her mother in the kitchen, or going to school, instead of messing about in a war.

Maria looked puzzled. She was Serbian, so it was natural that she should be helping her country, but what was an English woman doing so far from home, helping in a lost cause? Flora did her best to explain, but without much success.

Later that morning the young Greek doctor in charge of the Field Ambulance arrived and asked her to have lunch with him. He took her to a tiny loft over a stable a hundred yards up the road, which he had made his billet. It smelt of straw and cow-dung and wood-smoke. Underneath the wide floorboards four oxen moved restlessly in their stalls. The doctor spread out their meal upon a clean blue and white spotted handkerchief: a small loaf of bread, onions, cheese and hard-boiled eggs. He filled two chipped enamel mugs with red wine and shyly pushed one across to her. He was a pleasant young man, dark, with an eager, bird-like face. Later, when Flora discovered how scarce food was, she appreciated the gesture still more.

His name was Andros, and he was rather sad because he was Greek, and the Serbs were angry with the Greeks for not being in the battle on their side. He was a volunteer, but could see their point of view. After all, it was only two years since Greek and Serb had fought side by side to throw off the Turkish yoke. He was willing to die for Serbia, but what could Greece do when so violently pro-German a king was on the throne?

When they got back to the Field Ambulance after lunch, three heavy, dirty ox-wagons had arrived. They were two-wheeled vehicles, their rough-board interiors filled with grubby straw, and flimsy roofs fashioned out of a piece of canvas. They were pulled by draught oxen, huge velvety-eyed creatures, who stood there steaming patiently while the wounded were carried into the tent. Five walking wounded, gaunt and pale, were supporting themselves on the sides of the wagons. Maria was arguing with one of the men, and as the Doctor and Flora came up, she turned and asked for his support. The man said he could go no farther.

He was young. His leather sandals and stockings were coated with mud, his eyes were hollow and beaten, and he carried his right arm in a dirty sling. Flora felt sorry for him.

She intercepted a glance between Maria and the Doctor; the latter nodded and Maria went into the hospital tent. She reappeared with a bottle of brandy, gave him a long swig and passed it round to the others. Flora gave them two cigarettes each. After the brandy the young man nodded wearily and agreed to go on.

They set off again, the heavy wagons bumping and lurching along the road, and the walking wounded holding on to their sides. Andros assured her it was essential. They would be moving off at half an hour's notice within the next forty-eight hours. It might be dark, the weather might be bad; they all stood a much better chance of survival by reaching safety now.

The next forty-eight hours hummed with rumours and counter-rumours. Twice messages arrived for Flora from Mr Greig. The first came in the middle of the night and said: 'Strongly advise you return Monastir at once. Motor transport waiting for you in Prilep. Please inform messenger of your decision.' The second was a peremptory order for her to return.

She told the first messenger she had no intention of trying to find motor transport in Prilep in the middle of the night; the second that she had no intention of returning. She was a volunteer. And she was volunteering *to stay*.

Later that afternoon a Serbian officer arrived from Prilep. He brought with him all her remaining luggage, stowed in a small covered wagon drawn by a pair of horses. He said he would like her to accept it as a present from the Serbian army; they liked her spirit.

She was delighted with the gift. She and Maria filled the wagon with hay from a roadside rick and burrowed inside like a couple of happy dormice.

The order to retreat came at 10.30 that night. It was dark and moonless and the wind was blowing hard. Half an hour before the order arrived the rain began to drive down, and everybody was sodden and depressed. There were sixteen wounded to be got into the ox-wagons, and the orderlies left the main tent up as long as possible to allow them to keep dry. Just as they were about to strike it, a wounded soldier was brought into the tent by two stretcher-bearers. They lowered him into the straw and left him.

Using her own electric torch, the only one they had, Flora knelt beside him, cut away his stocking and the leather thongs holding his shoe. She examined the wound. A piece of shrapnel had entered his leg just above the ankle. It was a nasty gash, but there was no time to probe it. She poured in iodine and was still winding a bandage around his leg when Maria crouched by her side, wet and breathless, urging her to hurry. They must get him into the last ox-cart as most of the others had already left.

The two girls helped the soldier to his feet. He supported his weight on their shoulders. Flora heard his hiss of pain as he put his foot to the ground. They staggered to the back of the ox-wagon. Two soldiers already inside helped to pull him in. It was a dark hole smelling of wet straw, urine and sweat, but it was a shelter from the wind and rain.

They ran back to the cover of their own wagon, scrambled over the tailboard and huddled down into the hay as the driver shook up the horses. Flora shone her torch on to her watch. It was exactly eleven o'clock. It had taken exactly half an hour to strike camp and get on the move.

They dozed and chatted for the next two or three hours. Maria was nervous about passing through Prilep. She produced a hand-grenade from one of her pockets and sat with her finger through the release ring. As they rattled slowly through the darkened streets, Flora, who was far more scared of a mistake by Maria than any attack by the Bulgars, drew her own revolver. Together they peered over the tailboard not knowing what they might see. All was quiet and dark. When they were out on the open road again heading for Monastir, much to Flora's relief, Maria re-pocketed her grenade. The danger was over.

Flora lay back in the hay with Maria stretched out beside her. The hay smelt of summer; it was warm and soft, but the rain was rattling on the canvas roof and the wind blowing violently. Her blanket covered both of them. She offered Maria a swig from her water bottle and chuckled when she heard the girl gasp with surprise. A flask of brandy was as important as ammunition in your pouch, the old soldiers said. It would help them both to sleep.

They did sleep quite heavily as the wagon creaked and jolted through the night. Once they stopped, and, hearing a noise at the tailboard, Flora drowsily switched on her torch. It lit up the face of a young soldier. He was wounded, he said, and could walk no farther. Could he share their wagon? There was only room for the girls lying side by side, but he was welcome to a few inches. He climbed in and coiled up at their feet. Then she went to sleep again.

When she woke, it was daylight and the young soldier was just clambering out of the back of the wagon. He jumped lightly to the ground and suddenly she remembered that he was supposed to be wounded. He smiled at her and called out something she did not catch. She had been taken in but it didn't really matter. At least he had kept their feet warm.

Sunrise came at seven o'clock and the Field Ambulance unit halted. They were about twelve miles north of Monastir and, until a messenger arrived from Colonel Militch, Commander of the Regiment, they did not know whether they were supposed to continue or not. They sent the wounded ahead in an ox-cart to the town.

Flora was curious to meet the regiment's Commanding Officer. She asked Maria about him, but she had only seen him once and then from a distance. Both girls climbed out and stretched their arms and legs. The rain had stopped. The air was crisp and cold, the grass still wet and sparkling. They rinsed their grubby hands in it and wiped their faces. The orderlies gathered around to chat and gossip, and Flora, looking at their tired, unshaven faces, realised she must look pretty bedraggled herself.

No one knew what was happening. Occasionally from behind them and over to the east they heard the distant thunder of artillery. Everyone was hungry. There was no food, no brandy even, because when Flora came to examine her flask, she found the stopper must have fallen out in the straw.

She did not really care. Even without the brandy she felt warm inside. She was in battle. Only an unimportant member of a Field Ambulance Unit, but in battle, all the same.

III

It began to snow at six o'clock. The wind dropped, and the white flakes muffled the horses' hooves in the tiny courtyard outside and the rumble of the guns.

Inside the cramped two-room inn which was serving as regimental headquarters, the snow rapidly caked on the small window-panes, shutting out the growing darkness. Colonel Militch's orderly came in, lit the lamp and made up the small log fires.

The Colonel stretched across the table and poured another measure of brandy into Flora's glass. He was a man of medium height in his early forties; his black moustache was neatly trimmed and his hair was greying at the sides. When he smiled, he revealed his even white teeth, and he told her that her Serbian was improving when she replied '*Givelo*', and raised her glass to him. She had known him now for three days.

He had been a professional soldier all his life. For the past three years he had been almost continually in action and, as a realist, knew that his own chances of survival were negligible. In Belgrade he had left a wife and daughter; his two sons were both fighting with the Serbian armies in the north. Those armies and his own family were cut off now by a wedge driven across the country by the Bulgars.

This knowledge made no difference whatever to his military attitude or determination. Since the first offensive his regiment had been constantly on the retreat, making the enemy pay for each yard of ground with dead, counter-attacking when they could, and leaving small defensive rearguards as living sacrifices to gain for the others a brief respite and a further retreat.

He looked with interest at the English girl who had chosen to share their battlefield. He had not met a woman like her before: emancipated, outspoken, direct and yet still feminine. She intrigued him. She was quite unlike any Serbian woman he had ever known. In Belgrade a woman's place was still a minor one and the thought that she might be worthy of equality with men was too preposterous to be considered.

This woman rode as well as any of his officers and accepted hardship like any Serbian soldier. She worked tirelessly for the wounded, she was cheerful and amusing and yet remained a civilised, intelligent woman. Above all, she was English. That was important, because she represented those Allies without whom his country would never regain her freedom. He knew that they were on the brink of utter defeat; that these rearguard actions were improvised defensive measures to give the refugees time to move farther south, in the hope that fresh French or English battalions might suddenly appear at the railhead at Monastir and reinforce his own exhausted men.

As soon as the Bulgars brought up their artillery and exerted pressure, he would once again have to give the order to retreat. Unless he did so, the 2nd Regiment would be annihilated.

Flora sipped her brandy and peeped over the rim of her glass at Militch. It was strange to think that only three days ago she had been waiting at the roadside with the Ambulance Unit, when the Colonel and his staff rode up. He had dismounted and Andros had introduced them. One of his officers had produced coffee, the Ambulance Unit had provided boiling water, the Colonel had contributed a bottle of liquor, and they had all enjoyed a hot drink.

When he rode away, she thought how lucky the regiment was to have such a friendly man in command. Nevertheless she was a little surprised an hour later, when the Adjutant, Captain Stoyadinovitch, rode back and told her that the Colonel would like to have her attached to the other Ambulance Unit stationed at his headquarters.

Flattered, but a little sorry at having to leave Maria and Andros, she loaded up her covered wagon. She was taken by the

Captain to his temporary headquarters, a small dilapidated inn by a fast-flowing stream. Here she met Serge Konstantin, the young regimental doctor. He was handsome and elegant and delighted to have a pretty English nurse on his staff. He was also, as she was to discover, highly competent and very serious. There was little nursing to be done at the moment, he told her; they had hardly any medical supplies and very little chance of moving a badly wounded man to the rear. The Bulgars had not made contact after the last retreat, and the bad weather was obviously hindering their advance.

Flora found herself attached as a sort of supernumerary to the Colonel's staff. The Colonel lent her his second horse, a milk-white mare called Diana, and took her with him on several visits to the forward posts. She was present at staff meetings and listened to him giving orders over the telephone. She understood very little of what was being said because her Serbian was not yet good enough, but she realised that they were holding on by their fingertips, and that they did not expect to be able to hold on much longer.

The Colonel explained some of the details to her. As he spoke perfect German, they could converse easily. She asked him when the retreat would end. Would the Army be forced out of Serbia altogether? Would they surrender?

The Colonel did not reply immediately. He went over to the fire and kicked a log into place. When he came back he said they would never surrender. They had already been offered a separate peace by Germany and Austria and had contemptuously refused it. They would fight on to the borders of Serbia and beyond them through Albania to the sea, if necessary. Britain and France must eventually come to their help. If they were driven out of Serbia, they would fight their way back with French and British aid. This was nothing new for the 2nd Regiment. In the Turkish War of 1912 they had twice been wiped out almost to the last man, but they had recruited more men and returned to the battle. They would do the same again.

Sensing that she was troubled, he asked about her own future. She was English, she could leave at any moment. There was nothing for her to worry about even if they were forced out of Serbia.

That wasn't the point at all, she tried to explain. 'Don't you see,' she said quickly, 'I want to stay with the 2nd Regiment!' She watched Colonel Militch stare into his glass as if it contained some secret of the universe and heard him say grimly, 'You understand that, if we retreat through Albania, no ambulance wagons or vehicles of any sort will go with us. The wounded will be left behind. Crossing those mountains in mid-winter will be a terrible ordeal. Only the strongest will survive.'

'I want to stay with the 2nd Regiment,' she insisted. He swirled the brandy around in his glass and smiled gently. 'You are a civilian nurse,' he said, and paused as if a new idea had struck him. After a few seconds he said thoughtfully, 'I suppose you could join the Army.'

Flora stared at him in astonishment. Did he mean that she could actually join the army as a *real* soldier?

That was exactly what he meant. Serbian women were allowed to join the army, and many were already serving. Of course they were *Serbian* and he didn't quite know what the situation would be if a foreigner wanted to join.

'But we're Allies,' said Flora anxiously. 'You said so yourself.' He reflected for a few moments and nodded, with a half-smile. He would have to get the recruitment confirmed at Monastir with the Divisional Commander.

Flora stood up, excited. She saw his fingers fumble with the small, silver regimental number 'two' pinned to his shoulder epaulette. He unfastened it. 'Sandes,' he said briskly, 'stand to attention.'

She stood up as straight as she could. It was one of the great moments of her life. The Colonel stepped forward and pinned the small silver number to her khaki jacket.

'Private Flora Sandes, I welcome you as a new recruit to the 2nd regiment of the 1st Serbian Army,' he said gravely. He stepped back and saluted her.

'Now,' he said, 'I think a drink to my latest recruit is in order.' She sat down, dazed with happiness. Yet, oddly enough she felt no different. There she was, a real private soldier in a real army, yet she felt no different! Except that suddenly she was very happy and relaxed.

Ten minutes later Militch was called into the room next door which served as a telephone exchange.

In a few minutes he returned, looking grave. The Bulgars had returned to the attack. They would be leaving very soon. She had better see that her wagon was ready to move.

Flora found the Colonel's batman already loading her baggage, but she had no intention this time of riding in the wagon. As a member of the Serbian Army she intended to ride Diana, the horse the Colonel had lent her. As his latest recruit, she had already decided that her place was beside him on all possible occasions.

When all was ready, she went back to the fire to wait for something to happen. Nothing did.

It was a side of war that she had never expected : the waiting, the endless waiting. She talked to the batman and tried to improve her Serbian; that was one thing she could always do while waiting.

Two hours later Colonel Militch came stamping back into the room, shrugging off his overcoat, and shaking his hat free of snow. They were not leaving that night, after all, but at dawn. The path they would take was through the mountains and could not be enfiladed by the enemy.

The orderly had a blanket ready for her, so she did not bother to unpack her bed and sleeping-bag. She wrapped herself in it and lay down near the fire. The batman did the same. It seemed only a matter of minutes before he was shaking her gently by the shoulder. She sat up slowly, stiff and cramped, and glanced up at the grey light filtering through the snow and ice caked around the window. The batman produced a tin mug half-full of scalding tea, and she sipped it gratefully.

Outside a watery sun gleamed through the haze. The mountains looked hard and comfortless against the banked clouds. Diana snorted and stamped her feet and blew long plumes of steam down her nostrils. When they set off along the narrow trail, it was hard-packed with snow where the wagon wheels and horses' feet had trampled it down, and stained here and there with dung or urine.

The track descended steeply down the fir-clad hillside winding across a small log bridge. Beneath the bridge raced a mountain stream, its sides fretted with ice. As they passed beneath the overhanging firs, flakes of snow floated down on to their heads, and sometimes a small avalanche slithered to the ground from the higher branches. In front and behind stretched the dark figures of the retreating army.

It was not a long journey. After two hours they halted at another small and deserted hut by the roadside. A thick snowstorm suddenly came howling down the mountainside and the air was filled with whirling flakes. She edged her horse under the shelter of the eaves and pulled her scarf up over her face so that only her eyes were uncovered. Then she saw a body of troops floundering up the road towards them.

Since dawn there had been occasional distant rifle shots, but now the noise of firing seemed much closer. The men broke step as they reached the house and went tramping down through the deep drifts and the screen of trees which led to the open country. One of them, no more than a boy, passed quite close to her and waved cheerfully. His cap was set jauntily on his head and he had his rifle at the ready.

Then Flora heard a sound which set the nape of her neck tingling. The blizzard had blown itself out; the sun was shining again when, on the wind, faint and distant, she heard the sound of men shouting. It was not so much a shout as a chant, a distant '*Houra-Houra! Houra!*', the battle cry of the Bulgars as they charged into action!

It scared Flora, and she looked across at the Colonel. The rest of the officers, six in all, were standing in their stirrups to see what was happening. The slow procession of ox-wagons and horse-drawn carts and weary soldiers had passed out of sight down the road. They were the actual rearguard.

The Colonel at their head, they jogged up to a high point of land which looked out over the countryside. The sky was cloudless, the air was crisp and clear and, far below, perhaps a mile away, Flora saw the battle.

Across the white plain, dotted with bushes and rocks, moved an extended line of tiny black ants. She knew that these were the Bulgars advancing methodically across the snow. The Serbs lay or knelt behind the cover of a bush or rock, firing at the advancing enemy. Occasionally the line would hesitate, then two horns would creep out around the isolated point of resistance, black spots would suddenly dart forward, and a tiny group of ants would flurry in the snow. Then the line would re-form and move onwards again.

Flora's stomach felt hollow, her mouth dry. She realised that the body of troops which had tramped down the snowy hillside had gone to form yet another hopeless pocket of resistance. The young man who had waved so gaily to her would probably soon be dying in the snow so as to give a little more time to his retreating comrades.

This was war and this was what she must endure from now on. It would probably be much worse. All her joy and pride at being a soldier seemed to shrivel inside her. It was just as well, perhaps, that she did not at that moment understand the full extent of her commitment. Not only was she in the middle of a battle, but she was also about to take part in a tragic retreat, unparalleled in the history of the first world war.

Chapter Four

I

IT WAS bitterly cold, and Flora pulled her muffler closer around her mouth as she rode through the dark and deserted streets of Monastir at the side of Colonel Militch. The snow deadened the sound of the horse's hooves, and on the sloping roof-tops thick layers of it were reflected beneath the pale glare of the moon and the high cold stars. Icicles hung from the eaves, and below in the passageways the shadows were black and impenetrable. Occasionally there was a yellow flash across the sky and a distant rumble revealed an enemy battery. In a narrow street, they dismounted and entered the house where the Divisional Commander had set up his H.Q.

They found him in the dining-room, a long draughty place with dark oil paintings of somebody's ancestors hanging on the walls, and a long table down its centre. An oil lamp on the sideboard flickered slightly as the door closed behind them. Colonel Wasitch looked old and worried: a short square man with iron-grey cropped hair, his shadow cast grotesque patterns on the walls and ceiling as he paced up and down, watched anxiously by his aide, a young man in a major's uniform, and a British officer who was introduced as Captain O'Grady of the British Military Mission.

As he clarified the position incisively, Flora began to realise that her newly-acquired status as a private was in jeopardy. She had a feeling that he was trying to get rid of her.

By daylight, he said, the last units of the Serbian Army would evacuate Monastir. The last train which could conceivably get through to Salonika before the line was cut left at midnight, in three hours' time. He paused and looked at her, obviously suggesting that she had time to catch this train. The idea depressed her utterly, and she stared across at Colonel Militch, seeking his moral support. He did not look at her. She glanced at Captain O'Grady, but he avoided her gaze also.

At last Colonel Wasitch sat down at one end of the long bare table and drummed on it with his fingers. She must understand: he wanted her as a soldier in his army; he had nothing but admiration for her courage in volunteering; but the prospect of these terrible mountains would, by comparison, make all they had already experienced seem like a summer holiday. He did not have the right to expose her, a British subject, to such an ordeal.

Flora drew in her breath. She knew that she must make some energetic protest or she would be bundled unceremoniously aboard the train to Salonika.

She started off hesitantly. If the Divisional Commander felt that a woman would only be a nuisance, then she would get on the train and go back to Salonika without a word. However, she would like to mention that she had done some service to the army as a nurse in various hospitals both at base and in the field. Surely every pair of willing hands was of use? They would all live to fight another day; and whed that day arrived she wanted to be there to help continue the fight.

She said all this quietly and dispassionately, though she wanted to cry out and tell them that all her life she had sought for a cause like this to fight for, and now, at last, she had found one. Yet at this most vital moment in both their histories they were evacuating her, like a schoolchild, to a safe area.

She did not care what sacrifices she had to make; if they abandoned her now, they would break her heart.

The shadows flickered across the ceiling. The ancestors stared down with dead, fish-like eyes from their gilt frames. There was a long pause before Colonel Wasitch replied. Then he continued patiently, excusing himself by saying that there was nothing he would like more than that she should accompany them. The only hope left to the soldiers on their long journey across the mountains was a chance of fighting again alongside their Allies, and of fighting their way back to their homes and families. Very few of them knew much about England or France; most of them had never even seen an English woman. Therefore, Flora Sandes was a symbol that England and France had not forgotten Serbia. However, there were other considerations.

Colonel Wasitch stood up again, deeply concerned by the decision he had to make. He had no right to ask such a sacrifice from her, he said. She might die on this journey. Many people would die. He knew it would be an unprecedented *Via Dolorosa* across the mountains and that individual stories of suffering and heroism would be lost in the flood of misery. She had a chance of escape : she must take it.

The exodus of the armies and people of Serbia began during the winter months of November and December and continued into the New Year of 1916. From the first moments of the new invasion in September 1915, when over three hundred thousand fresh troops from Austria and Germany under the veteran Field Marshal, Von Mackensen, together with an equivalent number of Bulgars, attacked two hundred and fifty thousand Serbs, war-weary, ravaged by typhus, short of clothes, food, ammunition and weapons. Serbia, as a military force, was doomed.

The Serbs fought heroically; they bitterly contested every yard of ground. Because of the momentum of the enemy advance, most of the civilian population in the north were left behind, but, as the fighting drew nearer the southern and eastern borders, long columns of civilian refugees converged on the mountain passes leading into Montenegro and Albania. They were determined to cross the snowbound mountains rather than live under tyranny.

Within weeks the Bulgars had driven a wedge across the country, splitting the home forces in two, isolating the main army groups in the north and leaving the 1st Army to attempt to keep open one last escape-route to the south.

The northern army groups fought their last defensive battle upon the plain of Kossovo, known for five hundred years as the 'Field of the Blackbirds', commemorating a defeat by the Turks as bitter as the one they now faced. On November 27, after almost fifty days of savage and incessant fighting, the Schumadia Division stood before the town of Prizen, almost starving and practically without ammunition. Here they fought the enemy to the last bullet and the last shell to allow the refugees time to stream into the mountains.

The peasants left their farms, the women their kitchens, the children their class-rooms; the priests left their monasteries and churches, carrying with them coffins containing the bodies of mediaeval kings. King Peter, crippled by rheumatism, took his staff and walked through the mountain passes, and, when he could walk no farther, they carried him. With the long column of refugees went the aged Prime Minister, Pasich, and his Government, and the old chief of staff, Putnik, in a sedan chair, because he too was unable to walk. The Crown Prince Alexander, struck down with appendicitis, was taken into a cottage and operated on by his doctors. Bandaged, and bound to a stretcher, he was hauled over the mountains.

Of the two hundred and fifty thousand soldiers who were to make the journey, a hundred thousand died; of the half-million refugees who attempted the flight, two hundred thousand died; of the thirty-five thousand boys near military age, more than twenty thousand died, and of the sixty thousand Austrian and German prisoners whom the enemy authorities had refused to exchange through normal international channels, only a handful staggered down from the mountains to the Adriatic.

All this, however, lay in the future. In that long shadowy room, lit by a single lamp, its windows overlooking the silent snow-covered city, Flora Sandes knew that her entire future was at stake. There was more passion in her voice now, as she reiterated her reasons for wanting to stay. She understood Colonel Wasitch's arguments; they were clear-cut and rational. But was this a moment for rational discussion? Any rational foreigner would have quit this area long ago. She did not consider herself a foreigner. The cause of Serbia was close to her heart. Colonel Wasitch himself had stated that as a symbol she was of some use to his troops. Therefore she should be allowed to stay with him and with her regiment. She would catch the train, but only if she was given a direct order.

At this moment Colonel Militch left his place at the bottom of the table where he was standing with the aide and Captain O'Grady, and approached the Divisional Commander. He leant over to him and they conferred in whispers. Flora, not wishing to overhear, walked down the table and stood by O'Grady. He was a dark, good-looking Irishman in his early thirties and he bent towards her and whispered, 'Good luck'.

Two minutes later Colonel Militch straightened. He smiled down the table at Flora, and she wondered what he had told the Divisional Commander.

She watched Colonel Wasitch pat his colleague on the arm and stand up. He smiled at her and cleared his throat. 'Private Sandes,' he said, 'I have considered your request, and my doubts have been overcome both by yourself and by your commanding officer. Therefore I have great pleasure in officially ratifying your recruitment and rank in the 2nd Regiment, and I wish you every success in the future.'

He came forward to shake her hand and Colonel Militch, smiling broadly, followed suit. Captain O'Grady clapped her on the back. Flora could barely contain herself. Now she really was a soldier.

II

They left Monastir just after midnight, Flora riding Diana, the Adjutant by her side. They rode all that night and most of the next day. They rode slowly through a white countryside along roads choked with soldiers, donkeys and pack-horses, and they dismounted every hour or so at roadside fires lit by the advance party. There they stamped their feet and clapped their hands, trying to restore enough circulation to remount their horses. The road in places was a sheet of ice, and the Adjutant's horse fell so many times that eventually he had to get off and lead him. Flora slid off Diana. She was glad to walk for a bit; at least it nursed a little feeling back into her frozen feet.

By daybreak they had reached the mountains and begun the first slow climb up into the heights. Every few yards along the route lay the swollen corpses of horses and donkeys, ponies and oxen. Many had their hides and flesh stripped away.

At the side of the road lay many who had gone as far as strength or courage would take them: bundles of rags that had once been human. They were mainly children and old men. Their faces were covered with bits of rag or sacks, and sometimes an attempt had been made to scrape a little earth or snow over their bodies.

Flora wondered why she was not moved to despair. Long afterwards she decided it was because she had no time to pause or reflect. Life was a matter of getting enough to eat, of staying warm and of keeping on the move.

Before they left, Colonel Militch explained that she would be accorded two privileges unknown to the average Serbian private: a horse and a batman. Dragutin was to be her batman.

Two days after the battle in the snow the Colonel and his staff were billeted in a small house on the outskirts of Monastir.

A priest blesses new recruits at a swearing-in ceremony

Serbs dance the 'kola' with Allied comrades on the Second Regiment's 'Slava' (birthday)

Serbian cavalry ford a river before crossing Albania's mountain border

THE TRAGIC RETREAT

The Serbian Army mixed with refugees straggling through snow-locked passes

Few horses survived the nightmare trek

THROUGH ALBANIA

Chief of Staff Putnik, too old and infirm to walk, is carried to safety in a sedan chair

Flora Sandes, convalescing in Salonika after being badly wounded in the front line, wears her newly awarded Kara George Star

Survivors from the disastrous retreat are landed at Corfu

Jovitch and his company record their gratitude to "esteemed Miss Sandes"

4. Comp. 1st Battl. II-inf. Rgmt.
No 1024 (official Stamp)

To Miss Sandes, corporal, volunteer of this Company

Please receive this little, but from heart of my soldiers, declaration of thankfulness for all (for help) that you have done to them until now, and in time, when they are far away from dear ones and loving ones at home.

To their wishes and declarations I am adding my and exclaim:

Long life to our dear ally England,
Long life to Serbian heroic Army.

Comandant of the Company
Lieutenant
Janachko A. Jowitch

13/26 February 1916.
Ipsos (Corfu)

To High esteemed
Miss Flora Sandes
Corfu.

Esteemed Miss Sandes!

Soldiers of 4th Company 1st Battallion II. Inf. Rgmt. „Knjaza Mihaila", Moravian Division, I (call) Reserves; touched with your nobleness, wish with this letter to pay their respects - and thankfullness to you; have choosen a committee to hand to you this letter of thankfulness.

Miss Sandes!

Serbian Soldier is proud, because (for) in his middle he sees a noble daughter of England, whose people ~~are~~ is an old Serbian friend, and today their armies are, arm in arm, fighting for common idea, and you Miss Sandes should

British Tommies help a V.A.D. nurse change an ambulance tire near Ostrova Hospital

Marshal Mishitch, Commander of the Serbian Army, inspects the Guard of Honour after General Milne, C.-in-C. British Forces in Salonika, presents him with G.C.M.G. on behalf of King George V

The Second Regiment leaves Salonika and moves up to the front in northern Greece

With Major Tzoukavatz and Sergeant-Major Milosh, Sergeant Sandes enjoys a coffee during a pause in the advance

Flora (extreme left, back row) with her company outside Salonika. Lieutenant Jovitch is in front row, centre

It had two storeys, with one room on each floor, and a large balcony attached to the upstairs one. It was roofed over and piled at one end with fresh straw. Flora eyed it and decided she would be more comfortable in her sleeping-bag in the straw than with six snoring officers in a stuffy room.

The officers were very perturbed. She would freeze to death, they declared. Flora retorted that she had often slept in the open in her sleeping-bag, but they were not convinced. They had heard, however, that the English could be eccentric and did not protest overmuch.

Next morning Dragutin arrived. He was very agitated. What had she done? She had slept outside in the straw like a common peasant, when all those beautifully warm officers and gentlemen lay inside. Did she not know the distress this caused him? Did she not understand that if she continued to behave in this common manner, Dragutin would lose all respect from the other orderlies? Did she not understand that all Serbian batmen were volunteers, and that he had volunteered as batman to a *woman*, because he knew she was a very brave lady and a very English lady. This sort of behaviour was *not* ladylike. In these matters she must in future be guided by him.

Dragutin was twenty-seven years old and five feet three inches in height. His most striking features were his eyes. They were dark and intense, beautifully expressive, set in a face with a hairline that began two inches above heavy eyebrows, a nose that loomed craggily above the dark blue of his chin, and a mouth that turned downwards at the corners. It was a conspirator's face, but nature had given him the heart of a gentle old washerwoman.

Flora was indignant. If Dragutin thought she had to endure six snoring officers and a stuffy room merely to satisfy his sense of propriety, he had better start thinking again. She would sleep when and how she pleased, and, if he was so interested in her welfare, then he could start by finding her enough hot water to have a bath somewhere.

Dragutin walked away, glowering and unrepentant. He did, however, find her a stable, where he set up her rubber bath and filled it with some tolerably hot water.

She wedged the door with a piece of stick, wallowed for half-an-hour, and then spent ten minutes running lighted matches up and down the seams of her vest to cremate the lice. It was an old soldier's trick, but she wasn't very good at it, because she burnt two holes in her vest before Dragutin knocked to say that Mr Greig, the British Consul, had called to see her.

He was leaving for Salonika and had come to say goodbye. With him he had brought a case of cigarettes, another of jam and a third full of woollen balaclava helmets. He hoped she would be able to find some use for them.

After he had gone Flora consulted Major Pesitch, the C.O. of the 1st Battalion, and asked if he knew of any regiment which might like them.

He did. The 4th Company were camped only a couple of miles away. They had been drawn out of the line for a short rest and had had a very rough time; they would welcome a few pots of jam, balaclavas and cigarettes. He was going on a tour of inspection and he would show her their camp. Dragutin could drive out the wagon with the cases.

The 4th were camped in a low hillside covered with pines. It had snowed heavily the night before and the trees and the ground were covered to a depth of more than six inches. The tents were thick with snow too, and narrow foot-trodden tracks led between them to clearings where great fires of pine-boughs were blazing. Tongues of scarlet flame leapt high against the black trees and grey sky.

They walked their horses through to a clearing where many of the tracks converged and where three officers were standing round a fire. They came smartly to attention and saluted as Major Pesitch reined to a halt. Dismounting, he introduced Flora to the senior officer, Lieutenant Janachko Jovitch, who commanded the 4th Company.

Jovitch was about six foot, broad-shouldered, tough-looking and compact. Above his firm, broad mouth he wore a clipped black moustache, and his chin was large and competent. He wore no hat and his cropped hair bristled; beneath his black, semi-circular eyebrows, his dark blue eyes stared into hers with a direct and, so Flora thought, rather unfriendly gaze. He shook her hand and clicked his heels.

Major Pesitch introduced her as an English woman who had been accepted into the regiment as a private soldier and had brought out 'comforts' for the company. Jovitch nodded and introduced his two junior officers, Second Lieutenant Zaphir

Doditch and Second Lieutenant Aleska Vukoye. Their reactions were immediately friendly, quite unlike that of their superior officer; their handshakes warm, their smiles welcoming. Both of them, Flora judged, were in their middle twenties, Jovitch in his thirties.

Doditch was blond, rather fragile and poetic-looking. Aleska Vukoye was a tall, thin young man with a long, narrow face and a big nose; his cheeks were hollow and he was very dark. Major Pesitch made his excuses and remounted his horse. He would be back to collect her within an hour, he said.

Flora looked uncertainly at the three men and at the dozens of others all round, who were peering from their small bivouac tents. It was strange being left alone with about two hundred men. However, all three officers spoke German very well and with her bit of Serbian it was not hard to make conversation. Except with Lieutenant Janachko Jovitch. She caught a gleam of contempt in his eye as he glanced at the regimental number '2' she wore on her shoulder straps, and she turned away to talk to Doditch and hide her annoyance. If he didn't like her, there was nothing she could do about it, but she would be glad when Dragutin arrived so that she could get the job over and done with.

Her covered wagon came slowly through the trees, its wheels leaving deep ruts in the snow. Dragutin jumped down and threw open the canvas flaps so that Doditch and Vukoye could see what he had brought. While they were looking, Jovitch said in a quiet voice that it was indeed very kind of her to bring out all this jam and balaclavas and cigarettes. Did she think, however, there was any chance of rifles and ammunition arriving as well? It was very difficult to kill the enemy by throwing a pot of jam at him.

For a second Flora thought he was just making a bad joke, but when she turned to look at him she realised that he was deadly serious. Before she had time to answer, Doditch and Vukoye came back to ask for instructions.

Jovitch told them abruptly to parade the men and help her in any way she felt necessary. He would be in his tent if he was needed.

Doditch and Vukoye glanced with some embarrassment at Flora; there was little they could do to disguise the rudeness of their superior officer but she smiled at them and said perhaps they'd better get started.

Vukoye paraded the chattering, grinning company of two hundred and twenty men in three ranks, and Doditch arranged a fatigue party to open the cases.

The soldiers' grins grew broader as Flora walked along the ranks handing out two cigarettes to each man and a woollen balaclava helmet to every seventh. Dragutin trailed behind carrying the jam, and, as each man in turn opened his mouth, he reached up with his spoon and ladled in two helpings.

Afterwards Doditch and Vukoye invited her to take coffee with them while she waited for Major Pesitch. They sat on logs of wood round the fire as the orderlies prepared thimble-sized cups of thick, black, scalding liquid.

Lieutenant Jovitch came out of his tent to join them and thanked her formally for bringing out the comforts for his troops. Flora, who had now completely recovered her good humour, said it was nothing. After all they were allies, weren't they?

She saw Doditch and Vukoye exchange a glance of amusement and both turned towards their senior officer. Obviously she had hit upon a subject about which there had been much argument. Janachko Jovitch turned to stare at her. Yes, they were supposed to be allies, he said slowly.

Flora said she did not understand. He now became quite aggressive. Why, for example, had the British and French systematically refused them permission to attack the Bulgars when it was obvious to any Serbian who was not deaf, blind, dumb or a half-wit that, as soon as the Bulgars were ready for war, they would attack the Serbs? Perhaps she could explain this to a simple Serbian Lieutenant?

Flora had already discussed this with a half a dozen other Serbs. She was just as puzzled as they were, but she knew they did not blame her personally, any more than she would blame them for some of the actions of their own Government. She thought, as Lieutenant Janachko Jovitch, that the French and British Governments had committed a monstrous blunder, but she was not going to admit it.

Perhaps, she said, it was obvious to all, except simple Serbian Lieutenants fighting in these mountains, that if you held the reins of government in your hands you had to make decisions which were never easy and often unpopular. Britain was engaged in global warfare. All over her Empire men were mobilising for war. This wasn't the only place in Europe where men were dying. Perhaps he hadn't considered that? Why should Britain risk embroiling herself and her Allies with yet another enemy, when there was the slightest chance that skilful diplomacy might keep Bulgaria neutral? He tried to answer, but she was not to be interrupted. She was willing to admit that the Allied diplomacy had not been skilful enough; if they had had women diplomats it would certainly have been a great deal better; but their intentions had been quite honourable.

The two young Lieutenants enjoyed the argument, but Jovitch glared at her. She began to suspect that as far as he was concerned there was nothing academic about their argument; he was deadly serious. It was all very well to talk about 'honourable intentions', he said, but did 'honourable intentions' feed his men? Did they provide a single shell or bullet? A hundred rifles were worth all the good intentions of both France and Britain put together!

Flora was furious, though she knew he was perfectly justified in making these remarks; and she was surprised that no one made them before; all the other soldiers had been much too good-mannered.

French and British divisions had already landed in Salonika, she retorted angrily. He must know that the French had been trying to fight their way across to link up with the 1st Army for the past two weeks; even *she* had heard the sound of their guns. But even she knew they had arrived too late. Eventually, driven completely out of Serbia and Macedonia, they would be forced to accept defensive lines across northern Greece.

This appeared to goad him still further. He stood up, towering over her, waving his arms so violently that Flora wondered if he was going to hit her. Why had not these actions started earlier? he demanded. The war had been going on now for almost a year and a half. They did not expect to have their fighting done for them; all they wanted was guns and ammunition, something to fight with, and they would be driving forward, instead of being chased out of their own country by barbarians they hated, whom they had defeated once before and who now, he knew, would be taking their revenge.

Flora smelt danger. It was all very well to argue, but now Lieutenant Janachko Jovitch was backing his arguments with personal experience, and she knew that the experience was probably savage and heart-rending.

They would take their revenge by burning and looting and killing, continued Jovitch, angrily stalking up and down. While they were sitting around this fire at their ease, wives and mothers and sweethearts were being outraged, fathers and sons executed. . . .

The thought was too much for him and he stopped in mid-sentence and sat down. Suddenly Flora yearned to take back all she had said, to reach out and comfort him, to say that she had not meant to defend an attitude in which she did not believe. It was too late. She had committed herself to her argument, and now the wound between them was probably too deep ever to be healed.

It was at this moment that Major Pesitch chose to return. He slid off his steaming horse, warmed himself at the fire, began to say something cheerful, then, sensing an atmosphere, brushed up both ends of his heavy walrus moustache with a grubby, nicotine-stained forefinger and glanced at them both with his small piggy eyes. Vukoye and Doditch filled the air with gay chatter, and Pesitch, scenting trouble, kept silent.

He rode beside her as they left the camp. Why the devil did Janachko Jovitch take it all so seriously? She was on his side; she was as deeply committed as he was. Surely her presence there made it plain?

'You had an argument with Jovitch?' asked Major Pesitch finally.

'Yes,' said Flora unhappily, 'it developed into a bit of a row.'

'What about?'

'Oh, I don't know. . . . How the British and French let Serbia down, by not letting them attack Bulgaria."

Major Pesitch nodded. Flora admired him: his robust sense of humour, his growling insistence on discipline and his practical humanity had made her warm to him.

He began to tell her about Lieutenant Jovitch. He was a rebel, he said, a rebel who believed fanatically in the future of Serbia.

'We old chaps,' said the Major, 'tend to lose our enthusiasm as time goes on, but not Janachko; the worse things get, the brighter he burns.'

Janachko Jovitch, he went on, had enlisted as a private when the Turkish War had started. Within three years he had risen from the ranks to the position of First Lieutenant. In the Serbian Army that meant you were a remarkable soldier.

As he spoke, he glanced across at her and she knew that he was trying, in his fatherly way, to excuse one of his junior officers. But Flora did not want him to defend Janachko Jovitch. He expressed exactly what she felt herself. She only wished she could have made that quite clear.

III

After leaving Monastir it took the 2nd Regiment four long days winding across the Macedonian mountains to reach the northern end of Lake Ochrid and the village of Struga.

In the late afternoon of the first day, they reached the highest point of the mountain road nearly 4,000 feet high and halted beside the ruins of a broken-down cottage. They had been on the move for more than thirty-six hours, and Flora knew they would have to halt soon, but she didn't think much of this as a place to camp. To her relief she heard that they were to spend the night in a village called Resen at the foot of the mountain.

The village was a large one. The main road through it was a sea of mud, and there was thick snow on the roof-tops. A large, square barrack-like building in the centre had been set aside for the officers and troops, but Dragutin quickly discovered a small house owned by two old ladies.

They welcomed Flora like a long-lost daughter and showed her upstairs into a pleasantly furnished room. She eyed the eiderdown and the white sheets uneasily. She disliked the idea of leaving lice in the bed and wondered how she could avoid it.

The old ladies were charming. They sat downstairs, hands folded in rather faded silk laps, pathetically anxious to talk of the outside world. They spoke only Serbian, and Flora occasionally missed some of their conversation. They seemed to have very little idea that a war was raging practically outside their front door, and didn't seem particularly interested.

Flora solved her sleeping problem by undressing completely and scrubbing herself all over before going to bed. She slept so well that she was late getting up the next morning.

The old ladies were disappointed to find that she was leaving; they had imagined that the Army was going to stay in Resen for months.

They left the village at nine o'clock in the evening, a long procession of horses, mules and donkeys plodding up the long slopes over the mountain ranges. It was a bright moonlit night and all around them, as they climbed higher, they could see the camp fires of soldiers dotted over the hillsides.

The Colonel was leaving rearguards at strategic points to slow up the enemy's advance, and there were constant halts while he made short detours with the Adjutant. Flora had expected to march all night and was surprised when, shortly after midnight, the whole party turned off the road and made for a block-house which stood on the mountainside. Long ago it had been a Turkish strong-point. Here she saw the signallers rolling in the telephone lines and guessed that this was to be their headquarters in some sort of defensive action.

Outside the block-house the ground was inches deep in mud. Inside, a stove glowed in the centre of the room and piles of dirty straw were strewn over the floor. Between twenty and thirty officers crowded into it and lay on the ground. She sat on a small bench next to Colonel Militch listening to him giving orders on the telephone. At last she found a space a little less dirty than the others and stretched out to sleep.

When she awoke, the room was hot. Everyone, including the Colonel, was now sprawled out fast asleep. Most of them were snoring. Only one huge bearded soldier was awake. His job was to keep the stove stoked up. It glowed red-hot in places and the room was stifling, but he kept cramming in more wood. Flora sat up and frowned at him. He looked across and said innocently, 'Is there anything you would like, English woman?'

Flora realised that there was no hope of keeping the temperature down and asked him if he would fetch a bottle from her saddle-bag on the white horse outside.

He nodded and picked his way over the sleeping men to the door. He returned a couple of minutes later with the Thermos flask the old ladies had filled with tea, to which Flora had added a fair amount of brandy.

She unscrewed the top, pulled out the cork and half filled the cup. She handed this to the soldier, who grinned, nodded his thanks and took a large swig. With a cry he spat out the scalding liquid and wiped his mouth with the back of his hand. 'Jesu!' he cried, 'but this is a miracle!' By what magic had this liquid which had been standing half the night in a saddle-bag in the freezing cold retained its heat?

Flora tried to explain the mechanics of a Thermos flask, but with little success. Ah, the white horse? Had she something to do with it? 'Was it her colour?' he asked. Flora tried hard not to smile. She tried to explain once more but gave up. As she turned over to get to sleep again, she felt quite certain he was going to spend the next ten years experimenting with different coloured horses until he found the secret.

She woke again at five o'clock. The inside of the block-house was now like a furnace. It almost became impossible to breathe. She got up, picked her way over the bodies, and walked along the little passage which led outside. The moon was now low in the sky, and the stars were bright. The snow stretched away in every direction in a vast, white expanse. She took a deep breath of exhilarating cold air. In the doorway of the block-house she found an old box and sat on it to wait for the dawn.

Sipping hot tea from the Thermos, she watched the stars disappear one by one as dawn came up. She wondered what First Lieutenant Jovitch and his two deputies, Doditch and Volkoye, were doing, and if she would ever see them again.

IV

At Lake Ochrid, across the unruffled surface of the water, the black mountains of Albania dominated the skyline. Here they would fight their last set battle against the Bulgars, and from Struga, the small town at the northern end of the lake and the last in Serbia, they would begin their long and bitter retreat.

Flora watched the fighting from a Turkish village a few hundred feet up in the foothills near the Albanian border. Colonel Militch had set up his headquarters in the village, but the Adjutant had expressly forbidden her to go closer to the fighting. This upset her because an artillery captain had invited her down to visit his battery, so she sat there, glowering, her back to a walnut tree. She hated being protected.

The sun shone and the weather was balmy. To her right, hemmed in by dark mountains, the vast expanse of the lake, nearly fifteen miles long and seven miles wide, stretched away towards the horizon like an inland sea. Its shores were fringed with thick, feathery reeds which hid an army of birds; each evening they swooped high into the air and cavorted against the dramatic sunset skies.

Struga lay three miles away, a pretty little town with red roofs, white walls and small hotels. Once it had attracted fishermen from all over Europe who tried from dawn until dusk to entice the fat brown trout who lived in the lake. Now the town was on fire. It was reached by a thin white road which circled the grassy, swampy edges of the water, and was now being shelled. Flora could see the black smoke drifting against the blue sky and the occasional tongues of yellow flame. She could see the shells bursting amongst the buildings and hear the faint, sporadic rifle fire. The Serbs would hold on in the town until nightfall, and then under cover of darkness they would retreat.

The Bulgars knew that the only way of escape was along the road towards the mountains and kept it under constant bombardment. A few small pieces of Serbian artillery, antiquated Czech guns which they had dragged behind them through the mountains, were in action in a wood about a mile below the place where she sat. But their position had now become practically untenable, because the enemy had found their range and for the past half-hour had been dropping heavy shells among the trees. Not long ago the regimental doctor Serge Konstantin had handed her a huge piece of shrapnel as a souvenir. It had fallen plumb in the middle of the men's soup tureen in the field.

It was such a confused war, Flora decided. Only five minutes before she had been presented with a posy of flowers and a handful of walnuts by two small girls from the village, then along had come Konstantin with his piece of shrapnel, two very different gifts.

The inhabitants of the Turkish village were quite friendly. The house in which she was billeted was owned by a cheerful Turkish farmer, his face as brown and wrinkled as the walnuts he offered her every morning. He wore sandals with turned-up toes, dark breeches, a white shirt with a lace front, a leather waistcoat and a scarlet fez: he seemed happily resigned to the fact that when the enemy reached his village he and his family would all have their throats cut. She nibbled a walnut thoughtfully and considered the future. He had the look of a man whom destiny had marked out for a long and happy life until at the end of it his wives buried him under one of his own walnut trees.

The last two days had been tinged with an air of unreality. It was so odd to walk through this pretty village in the late November sunshine with the mountains rising above and the lake gleaming below, and know that a dozen minor battles were being fought in the area.

The Colonel had explained their situation on the map. Most of the 1st Army and all the refugees who wanted to escape were already in the mountains. The Second and Fourteenth Regiments were acting as rearguards. They would leapfrog each other during the final stages of the retreat through Albania. The enemy had little respect for frontiers.

The King of Albania had given permission for the Serbian Army to cross his territory, but Colonel Militch doubted if the royal decree would permeate to the inhabitants of such a wild and mountainous region. They were likely to be hostile. The Albanians and the Serbs had never had much time for each other.

The 14th Regiment had already taken up defensive positions across the border in Albania. That night the 2nd Regiment would break off the engagement with the enemy, retire through the 14th and take up their positions farther back. The 14th would then reverse, the procedure, and so on, fighting all the way back to the sea, if necessary.

At three o'clock in the morning the headquarters party started off on the long journey to the frontier. It was late afternoon of the next day before they arrived. A cairn of stones marked the border and they reined their horses to a standstill. It was a bitter moment.

Behind them the mountains, though their summits were covered with snow, were still green. In the valleys between lay villages, farms and ricks that told of centuries of patient harvesting. Ahead, the mountains were slabs of sheer, naked rock, dark and formidable, and above them, bolsters of dark grey cloud. Flora glanced discreetly round at the faces of her friends. Colonel Militch, erect in his saddle, was staring out of grey, expressionless eyes; Captain Stoyadinovitch and Major Pesitch had faces of stone. Flora could not look at Serge Konstantin; tears were pouring down his cheeks. She wouldn't have thought he'd have cared about frontiers.

She wished desperately she could assure them that they *would* come back, that there *would* be a victory, and that she would be with them. But she knew it was impossible. She knew about so many of them now, about their families and friends, about the wives and children who were somewhere behind them in the hands of the hated enemy. She knew that a Serb feels homesick ten miles from his own village; and these men were now hundreds of miles from their homes and were going still farther.

They rode on in silence to a sentry's hut in a dark and gloomy valley. Here they slept wrapped in their groundsheets. She had abandoned her covered wagon in Struga; now she had only Diana and a pack-horse which Dragutin looked after.

The next afternoon she rode out with the Colonel to visit positions held by the 14th Regiment, but, as they came closer, they saw the soldiers coming down the mountainside. A Major from the 14th came up and talked earnestly to the Colonel. As the Major rode away, Colonel Militch explained that the enemy had made a rapid encircling movement. Troops had to be rushed ahead to a long gap in the mountain range to secure their way of retreat. Even if they managed to defend the gap, unless they got to the top of Mount Chukas—he pointed out the long ridge which dominated the skyline over to their right—before the Bulgars, the chances of either the 2nd or 14th Regiments reaching the coast intact were slender.

It was now almost dark and on the way back Diana slipped in the mud and threw Flora over her head. She got up with a splitting headache. Fortunately, when they reached camp, Dragutin had pitched her tent, and he made tea for her, insisted that she lay down for an hour and clucked over her like a hen. There was no time to relax, though; the race was on. At 9.30 that night the column made off towards Mount Chukas. They rode until midnight, slept till 3 a.m. and then moved off again through the long grey dawn. At last they came to the hillside where the 2nd Regiment was camped, and Major Pesitch reported to the Colonel for his orders. He told them that the 4th Company had already gone forward to hold the gap; he was about to follow to see what was happening.

Flora looked at Colonel Militch and asked if she could go with him. He nodded wearily. She rode behind Major Pesitch at the head of a long column of infantrymen, but two hours later when they reached the 4th Company's positions they were already retreating, slithering towards them down the mountainside. In the distance she heard the noise of rifle and artillery fire. The Bulgars were advancing and there was little they could do to stop them.

Most of the men remembered Flora and waved and shouted cheerfully. Several wore the balaclavas she had given to them, but she did not see Lieutenant Jovitch, or either of his two Second Lieutenants, Vukoye and Doditch.

It was almost dark and they moved a few more miles through the valley at the foot of the mountain before they camped. Flora hitched Diana to a tree and scraped a hole under a bush. She pulled her overcoat as tightly around herself as she could manage and tried to sleep, but it was cold and soon it began to rain. The water dripped down from the leaves and seeped into her hole. She was glad when at 3 a.m., while it was still pitch-dark, they got the order to move.

The rain was now persistent. Flora swung herself up into the saddle; everything she touched, reins, saddle, even Diana's mane, was stiff with frozen rain. She patted the mare's neck and fondled her ears and wished she could tell her that within a few hours she would be warm and dry in a stable with hay to eat and a place to sleep.

She still had her headache and felt stiff and bruised. The rain trickled down her neck and she felt so miserable she could have cried. She thought longingly of the house back in Thornton Heath. If only she could wallow in a deep hot bath, dress in clean clothes, sit downstairs before the fire while Annie came grumbling in with hot buttered scones and tea on a silver tray. If only she could do her hair and look in a mirror and become a woman again. Just for a few minutes.

Maybe she should have caught that last train back to Salonika and not got into this situation where she might be a burden to everyone? The thought so depressed her that she sniffed loudly, and it was only then that she noticed that another horseman had drawn up alongside her. A hand produced a flask and a voice said, 'Take a drink of this, you'll feel better.'

She did not know who it was, and was too tired to ask: she

raised the flask and took a long gulp. It was brandy. Gasping, she handed it back. The hand reached across again and the voice said, 'Here, take these, I have two pairs.' The hand held a pair of woollen gloves. With a small shock of pleasure and excitement, she realised that the horseman was Janachko Jovitch. Before she had time to thank him, he had urged his horse forward and disappeared into the darkness.

With dawn banks of rain-cloud lifted away, a watery sun filtered through the mist and a rainbow formed over one shoulder of a tree-lined hillside. They halted in the shelter of a wood, the rain stopped completely and a few birds chirped in the trees.

Somehow, during the night, Flora had lost both Major Pesitch and the Colonel; she was now in the middle of the 4th Company. With Dragutin she sought out Janachko Jovitch. She found him with his junior officers, Doditch and Vukoye, mesmerized by some beans bubbling in a black cauldron hung over a large fire, and Flora suddenly knew that she was hungry. The two junior officers immediately invited her to breakfast with them.

Spooning the beans rather noisily off her tin plate, her mouth full of bread, the smell of hot coffee and woodsmoke in her nostrils, she gained new strength. She looked across at Jovitch, not quite knowing what to say to him, wondering if he had guessed how depressed she had been a few hours ago, trying to think of how to thank him.

She caught his eye and smiled. He nodded absently and went on eating. 'More beans?' he asked casually.

'No thank you,' said Flora coldly. All right, then, she could be as distant as he was.

He dropped his spoon on to his plate with a clatter and looked across at her. He saw a tall, pretty girl, with a round, Serbian cap perched on her brown hair, her eyes tired, her face grubby, her overcoat creased and stained, yet still feminine. And it annoyed him. Women should not be mixed up in war. Women had their uses, but this one had no right to be eating their scanty rations and distracting them by just being there. He knew that both Vukoye and Doditch liked her, and this annoyed him still more. There was no time for this sort of nonsense. They had one overriding duty: to escape, to live and fight again; this strange English woman could only hinder them.

Last night he had intuitively sensed her distress and tried to help her. He expected her to feel tired and sick; it was quite natural, but this was a battle, not an excursion, and she should not be there at all. He would arrange, he said, to send a runner to find Colonel Militch and the H.Q. staff. The entire battalion was about to scale Mount Chukas. She could, of course, stay with the horses and baggage animals and some of the orderlies, if she preferred.

He watched her eyes open wide in annoyance. She banged her plate down noisily on top of his and stated that, as a properly accredited private in the 2nd Regiment, she had as much right to go to the top of Mount Chukas as all the other privates.

Jovitch could have slapped her. For a private to answer a Lieutenant in this manner was bad enough, but Mount Chukas was over five thousand feet high. It was a long hard climb to be made at speed; besides, when they reached the summit they might find the Bulgars in command, in which case the situation would be extremely unpleasant.

Did she think that this was some sort of picnic? He looked round at his company: two hundred and twenty of them, weary, dirty, belching, ruminating, scratching their armpits, yawning, spitting, stretching and swapping obscenities; peasants mainly and farmers' sons, with a sprinkling of electricians, plumber's mates, waiters, shopkeepers, errand boys and clerks. He knew and loved every one of them: Mancha, the machine-gunner who had served in the best hotel in Belgrade; Mirko, who had a fruit-stall in Nish; Miladin, a peasant farmer. But what was this English woman doing there? She was obviously a lady, educated and well-spoken, with fluent German and French, the sort of girl his mother had always hoped he would marry one day when the war was over, if ever it was over. But what did she know about life in the army? She might have worked in a hospital, but she'd still to see a man die with a bullet in his belly or his guts on the grass beside him. How would she react then?

He saw Vukoye trying to catch his eye. Jovitch allowed himself to be led to one side. Vukoye said he would look after her until they got to the top of Mount Chukas; after all she was the Colonel's guest; they could hardly be rude to her. Jovitch nodded. He knew that Vukoye was right. As he walked away to tell Rangel, the senior Sergeant-Major, to get the company on its feet and moving, he passed Sergeant Miladin who served in Vukoye's *vod*.

'Sergeant,' he said, 'this Englishwoman is coming to the top of Mount Chukas with us. You will look after her.'

Sergeant Miladin stood to attention, saluted, and said, 'Yes sir.'

The whole battalion set off on foot, fanning out across the mountainside, slowly climbing in extended order. Flora, with Lieutenant Vukoye beside her, hauled her way up through the bushes on the lower slopes, scrambled over rocks and boulders, felt the water ooze into her shoes, and wondered what would really happen if they got to the top and found the enemy in possession.

They rested every ten minutes, and during their short breaks Second Lieutenant Vukoye began to talk about Jovitch. Did she know that the Lieutenant had been wounded? He had a bad wound in his chest which was only partly healed, and a bullet in his side which the doctor had not managed to extract. That was why he was a little rude and impatient on occasions.

The 4th was not just another company in the Army, Vukoye went on, it was two hundred and twenty men cemented by a feeling of comradeship. Their first loyalty was to the company; after that came the regiment, and then the battalion. You couldn't know every man in a battalion, but you knew every man in the company like a brother. And that comradeship stemmed from good leaders. Any man in the 4th Company would die for Janachko Jovitch.

Climbing with powerful strides and apparently little effort a few yards away to Flora's left, was a giant of a man, lean, sinewy and tireless. On several occasions, smiling, he reached out and tugged her up the mountainside.

This was Miladin, Lieutenant Vukoye told her. He was a sergeant in his *vod*. The company was divided into four *vods* of approximately fifty men each. Vukoye was in charge of one, Doditch another, and there should have been two more officers, but casualties had been heavy, and the other *vods* were now led by sergeant-majors.

They reached the long ridge which marked the summit of Mount Chukas at four o'clock in the afternoon. There was no sign of any Bulgar patrols. The entire battalion sprawled on the wet grass, rested for a few minutes and prepared to spend the night there. Fifty yards below the ridge grew a swathe of pine trees among which the 4th Company camped. It was raining hard again now. Even beneath the pines there was not a dry spot. The tents were made of four pieces of mackintosh. Each soldier carried one piece and used it as a cape during the day, and if he couldn't erect his tent, simply rolled himself up inside it. This time, though, they were able to put up their tents and light smoky fires. Vukoye and Doditch shared one tent, the other belonged to Lieutenant Jovitch. She wondered if he would invite her to share it, and if he did, should she accept?

Jovitch produced some bread and cheese from his knapsack and divided it up. Flora ate hungrily, licking the crumbs from her fingers. When they had finished, Jovitch made no formal invitation. He simply motioned towards the tent, and Flora crawled thankfully inside. In the damp, dark hole, with its mackintosh walls, there was barely room for two people, but at least it was some sort of protection from the wind and rain. She turned on her side and tucked her overcoat around her; she felt Janachko Jovitch crawl in beside her, turn on his side and wedge his back against hers. She closed her eyes thinking that the last thing she had expected was to be sleeping with the Company Commander on her first night with the 4th.

She woke in the middle of the night. Her feet and knees were like ice; and she couldn't get to sleep again. She could hear the fire crackling and spitting, and deciding that she preferred warmth to shelter she wriggled outside. Jovitch did not stir.

She sat by the fire, huddled in her overcoat, letting the flames toast her face and body. High overhead the rain clouds raced by, but now there were great rifts of stars between their windtorn edges. Soon, feeling drowsy again, she turned on her side, pulled up her overcoat lapel to protect her face from the dripping trees, stretched her feet out towards the fire, and instantly fell asleep.

The light woke her. She opened her eyes, puzzled at first by the immense wash of rose-coloured sky. The rain had stopped and the sun was rising. She sat up, stretching her arms and legs, smelling the freshness of the earth, and to her joy, discovered her feet were warm. Five seconds later she found the reason: the fire had burnt both soles almost completely off her shoes.

Soldiers were moving about, and Vukoye stood yawning four yards away. Jovitch had disappeared. Vukoye asked if she had slept well, then went on to tell her that the 4th were now moving up to the mountain ridge again to relieve the company which had spent the night on look-out. She could come if she wished.

They laboured up the rocky slope and she found it hard to breathe. She reached the long jagged ridge of rocks and, panting, flung herself down on a patch of gravel beside Vukoye. The ridge was dominant: beneath the pale dome of the sky the mountains sprawled in all directions, but the shoulders of Mount Chukas which they now occupied stood highest of all. Sensing her exhilaration, Vukoye turned towards her and laid a warning hand on her arm. The dawn was often beautiful, he told her, but could also be malevolent. Against the sky, or a pale landscape, a man might suddenly be vulnerable to a sniper's bullet or a blast of machine-gun fire. Darkness concealed, daylight destroyed. She must always remember that.

No sooner had he finished speaking than from somewhere below them came the rattle of a light machine-gun. She peered downwards. Miles below in the valley, ants were moving among the rocks. The sun, tilting across a low saddle, revealed them as plainly as a searchlight. The Bulgars had arrived.

Vukoye's mouth tightened. He took her across to where Sergeant Miladin and his *vod* were waiting and left her while he went off in search of Jovitch. Miladin and twenty-five men were occupying a small natural hollow scooped out along the ridge. Beneath it the rocks fell sheerly for three hundred feet; it was a perfect defensive position. The men sat around with their backs against the rocks, a rough and unshaven crowd, but they all smiled cheerfully and seemed pleased to have her with them. They wore the rough, grey-brown, home-spun tweed uniforms of the Serbian Army: a short jacket buttoned at the neck, breeches and woollen stockings with a variety of flower-patterns around the tops. These were embroidered, she learned later, by mothers or wives or girl-friends, and much love and patience went into their making. Only a few possessed boots; most of them wore a sort of leather sandal fastened with thongs round their calves. All wore round sheepskin caps.

While they were waiting, she pulled out a tin of fifty cigarettes and passed it around. The platoon were delighted. Each man carefully extracted a thin cylinder of tobacco and inhaled it with slow reverence.

A minute or so later an order from Sergeant Miladin, who had been peering cautiously down into the valley, caused them to stub out their smokes, carefully stow the dog-ends away for later, and take up firing positions among the rocks. Flora was wondering what she should do, when she saw Miladin beckoning her forward. One soldier occupied a comfortable v-shaped niche in the rocks. Miladin tapped him on the shoulder and said, 'Mirko.' The man twisted round; he had a chubby, unshaven face, bright eyes and his lips parted to reveal white and regular teeth. Without a word he wriggled back, stood up and half bowed, gesturing like a waiter offering her a seat.

Miladin took his rifle and showed it to Flora. It was an ancient weapon, made in Czechoslovakia at the turn of the century. With a quick turn of his wrist Miladin manipulated the bolt, snapped a cartridge up into the breech and handed it to her. She had carried and fired many guns before out shooting, but this was the first one she had been given for the precise purpose of killing a man.

She hesitated, shocked. Sporadic rifle fire was now being directed from their ridge at the Bulgars down below and she guessed that they were trying to advance. Her mouth went dry. As she stretched herself out, she realised she had committed herself to this situation and she was frightened.

She inched forward and looked down into the valley. To her intense relief it looked empty. Then she saw far below a little puff of white smoke from behind a rock. As she stared, she saw another puff of smoke and then a third. A small figure detached itself from one rock, hurtled to another and disappeared. She was relieved to see how far away they were. It was clear that any concerted advance up the slope would be suicidal. She also felt it was about time she showed them whose side she was on.

She pulled the rifle hard into her shoulder, carefully aligned the blade of the foresight with the V of the backsight as she had been taught, focused on a distant rock and gently squeezed the trigger. There was a violent bang; the butt kicked against her shoulder with the force of one of Diana's hind hooves, and she felt enormous relief. She had fired her first shot in battle. It wasn't as bad as she had expected. The bullet had obviously bounced harmlessly off a rock miles down below, but it was symbolic of Flora's determination. She had declared herself.

She glanced back over her shoulder. Both Miladin and Mirko stood behind her, grinning approval. Flora decided they needed some sort of celebration. She sat up, pulled out her tin of cigarettes and tossed one to Mirko who caught it neatly, smiled and passed forward a handful of cartridges. She collected them into a small heap beside her, the brass shells glinting in the sunshine.

She saw Miladin's eyes riveted on the cigarette tin, so she held it out to him. He raised his eyebrows in a gesture of resignation, and said, '*Hvala*'. Thank you.

At that moment a bullet struck a rock and ricocheted with a whine. Instinctively she ducked and covered her head with her hands. When she looked up, Miladin was smiling down at her. He had obviously not moved.

Much later, when she could converse fluently in Serbian, he was to tell her that the bullet you hear is the friendly one; the bullet you don't is the one which kills you. He now gave instructions to the *vod*. She understood that at his word of command they were to fire in volleys. On the order '*Ne shanni!*' they would take aim, and at the command '*Balli!*' fire.

He snapped an order to the rest of the platoon and she heard the scraping of rifle-bolts. She pushed another cartridge into the breech and jammed the butt hard into her shoulder. Tomorrow her shoulder would be black and blue from the recoil, but she didn't care.

'*Ne shanni!*', he called.

Flora closed her left eye and laid her sights on the groups of rocks from which most of the puffs of smoke seemed to be coming.

'*Balli*!'

She squeezed the trigger gently and felt the rifle leap in her hands. The shots echoed and re-echoed in the valley like thunder. The order was repeated three times, and the echoes seemed to surround them.

Sergeant Miladin motioned to her to return her rifle to Mirko. She slid back and handed it over. The Sergeant stood there, his hands on his hips, a tall lean figure, the round, grey cap tilted back on his head and his moustache drooping down over his smiling lips. Flora suddenly noticed the little pink roses round the tops of his stockings, and wondered affectionately who had embroidered them.

They held their position all day, firing occasional volleys down into the valley, more as a threat, since it must have been obvious that their position was impregnable. They were due to be relieved at dark, but darkness fell and no relief appeared. The firing dwindled. Occasionally a light machine-gun far below would open up, shattering the quiet, but soon it stopped altogether.

It was much colder now. The sky was clear and the stars bright. Up on the dark ridge they blew into cupped hands and stared at the enemy's fires beginning to flicker on the far side of the valley.

From time to time a snatch of song would float across the bowl of the valley, once known only to shepherds, and now a dark no-man's-land between the two armies.

There would be no attack tonight, Miladin said. The Bulgars were content with their position and probably too tired to try and advance; the Serbs were grateful for the rest. A patrol might sidle out of the night and cut a throat or two, but the Serbs, veterans of a thousand cold and windy nights in the mountains, recognised the signs of a lull.

A whistle in the dark, the scrape of feet on rock, and they knew that their relief had arrived. It was good to scramble down the mountainside towards the glow among the trees. Sergeant Miladin led her to where Jovitch, Vukoye and Doditch were warming their hands around a blazing fire. The pine logs burned with an intense coral glow, and the light danced on the trunks of the tall trees. The orderlies had been at work piling heaps of fragrant spruce boughs round the clearing to act as beds. Flora collapsed on one of them gratefully. She watched Miladin talking quietly to Lieutenant Jovitch and she returned his smile as he saluted and disappeared into the darkness.

Several weeks later Jovitch revealed to Flora the gist of his conversation with Sergeant Miladin. He had asked the Sergeant how she had behaved, and Miladin had reported that she had acquitted herself well. She had fired a rifle like a veteran and never complained. And the men inquired Jovitch, how had they taken her? Miladin's answer had surprised him. The men had been delighted and flattered by her presence. They had shouted across to the other companies that the Englishwoman was fighting with *them*, boasting that she had obviously joined their *vod* because it was the best in the entire Serbian army. Before Miladin returned to his own camp fire, he looked Jovitch in the eyes and said respectfully that, if she was staying with the 4th, he would be glad to have her in his section. Jovitch watched his tall figure disappearing into the darkness and realised that he had made a hasty judgment. Colonel Militch, whom he admired above all other officers, had at once understood that her value far outweighed any trouble she might cause. In fact, if he was completely honest with himself, he had to allow that she had not been a nuisance at all. She had climbed the five thousand feet as well as any of them, she had obviously reacted under fire much better than could be expected, she had considerable prestige value, and last of all, although he did not then consciously admit it to himself, he was beginning to get used to her, if not actually like her.

He had talked earlier to both Vukoye and Doditch, and both had urged him to ask her to stay with the 4th. They were intrigued by her; she was original, they had never met anyone like her before. War was a grim business, she had come into it voluntarily, and anything or anyone that could add a touch of gaiety to their lives was invaluable. Besides, and it was upon this that they insisted, the 4th would look after her better than anyone else.

He produced the last of the bread and cheese for supper and they brewed sugarless Turkish coffee over the fire. Outside the small circle of firelight, the hoar-frost was white on the grass and the mountainside gleamed with silver in the starlight.

Dragutin had brought up a blanket for her and she snuggled down among the spruce boughs and tucked it around her legs. She looked across at Lieutenant Jovitch: the red glow of the fire deepened the lines in his face, making him look older and sterner. He caught her look and returned it. He mentioned that Sergeant Miladin had told him that he was willing to have her in his *vod*. Flora nodded gratefully. She knew Sergeant Miladin had liked her and she liked him.

She sat up in amazement and confusion as Jovitch continued. What was he saying? Would she like to enroll on the 4th Company's books and be attached to Sergeant Miladin's platoon under the *vod* command of Second Lieutenant Vukoye? Her eyes switched from one face to the other, certain that he was joking. Yes, Doditch and Vukoye were smiling, but Jovitch seemed quite serious.

Did he really mean that she could join the 4th Company as a private soldier?

Jovitch nodded solemnly. The sergeant was a good soldier and he respected his opinion. She would still be allowed a batman and a horse, and she could mess with them whenever possible. Otherwise she would just be an ordinary private sharing the same dangers and discomforts. Did she accept?

Accept! Flora could have shouted aloud for joy. To be a member of a fighting company in the best regiment in the Serbian Army, the Iron Regiment as they were nicknamed, was an honour she had never dreamt possible.

Good, said Jovitch. Then that was settled. After a period of probation, there was every chance that she might be made a corporal.

Dazed with happiness, Flora lay back upon her bed of spruce branches and stared up at the stars. After a little while Vukoye leaned over her and asked her what she was thinking about. For a few seconds she was silent. She recorded her reply in her diary: 'I lay on my back looking at the stars . . . I told him that when I was old and decrepit and done for, and had to stay in a house and not go about any more, I should remember my first night with the 4th Company on the top of Mount Chukas.'

Chapter Five

FLORA LIFTED the flap of her tent and walked out into the pale December sunshine. The rust-coloured bracken, which had provided them with soft beds for the past three nights, sparkled with recent rain, but above the snow-covered peaks a wide band of blue sky was spreading. She paused for a few seconds to let the sun's rays warm her face.

She passed between the rows of tents acknowledging the greetings of her company. '*Dobar dan* Sandes,' they called. Mirko, who was cleaning his rifle, waved his hand; she was beginning to know all their faces. She stopped to talk to Doditch, who was sitting sunning himself. It was Christmas Eve, she told him. She had just consulted the small calendar in her diary; she knew that the Serbian Christmas, something to do with the Roman calendar, came fourteen days later, but as far as she and most of Europe were concerned it was Christmas Eve.

Doditch stood up and called to Vukoye who popped his head out of the tent. Had he heard what she said? They must have a party.

It seemed almost impossible that less than a week ago they had been fighting on the top of Mount Chukas. They'd stuck it there until the day after Flora was enrolled as a private; then by late afternoon the Bulgars had brought up their artillery, and shells were dropping with disturbing accuracy on the Serbian side of the ridge.

The descent was long and tiring. They followed a track which seemed to be mainly composed of mud, and Flora, the soles of her shoes burnt away, slid down much of it on her back or behind. No one was more pleased to reach the bottom and find that Dragutin and the other orderlies had the horses saddled and waiting.

They rode and walked all through the night, a long weary, jingling procession of men and animals passing along a narrow defile through the mountains. They met the rest of the regiment just after daylight and built fires round which they sat for a couple of hours. They moved on again towards the Albanian town of Elbasan where they camped in a low-lying, swampy field. As they drew near, Jovitch swung in his saddle and shouted a word of command which was taken up all along the line by the sergeants. The weary men formed into a column, shouldered their rifles, got into step and with heads up and arms swinging marched into camp.

No one was sorry when, two days later, the 4th Company were ordered out of camp and into the foothills outside the town to dig in and wait for enemy patrols. The swampy field had been unpleasant. They made themselves comfortable, although rations were getting very short, and practically the only food they had left were mealie-cobs. But the sun shone, and the men were able to take off their shirts and wash and shave.

Two days passed and still there was no sign of Bulgar activity; Lieutenant Jovitch sent out patrols but they failed to make contact. The enemy, at least for the time being, appeared to have given up the chase.

That Christmas Eve they built a huge fire, and the entire 4th Company gathered around it. The party stirred when the Company cooks served up what Flora knew must be the last issue of bread and beans; it gathered momentum when Vukoye and Doditch passed around a number of bottles of the cheapest brandy, which they had managed to buy on an afternoon visit to Elbasan, and began to blaze when the *tzigane* violinists—every company had several on its payroll—got out their instruments and started to play.

Flora sat on a log between Miladin and Sergeant-Major Milosh. Each *vod* was divided into *decetars*, sections of ten men; Miladin commanded the 1st *decetar*, Milosh the 2nd. They were great friends but diametrically opposed in character. The violins shrilled; Dratza, a young man in Flora's *decetar*, led the choruses in a glorious tenor voice. He was one of the most handsome men Flora had ever seen, twenty-three, with deep blue eyes, white skin and tight dark curly hair, cheerful, lazy, happy-go-lucky and very popular. To hear him sing a sad Serbian song with a violin in the background was enough to bring tears to the eyes.

There was loud applause when he had finished and general

cheers for more. Miladin leant across Flora and slapped Milosh on the knee. What about a song from the Sergeant-Major? She soon discovered that making fun of Milosh, the disciplinarian N.C.O. of the regiment, was one of Miladin's favourite pastimes.

Miladin was six feet five inches tall, thin as a beanpole; he loped rather than walked, and coiled rather than sat. He had baby blue eyes, a sunny nature, a moustache which drooped like a Turk's and a persuasive way with his men. This, coupled with the fact that bullets seemed to try to avoid him, had earned him swift promotion to the rank of senior N.C.O.

Sergeant-Major Milosh snapped back a remark which Flora didn't understand, brushed up the waxed moustache which protruded from his upper lip and glared ferociously. He was forty and of medium height. His hat was always correctly set on his head, he was taciturn, unimaginative and inflexible. He had been born in a village close to the Bulgarian border and had experienced, since his earliest days, the raids of Bulgar *comitjades*. As a youth he had continually fought against them, and, since life seemed one long battle anyway, he had joined the army as a professional soldier. He had been on active service almost ever since. His old mother still lived in the village, but otherwise he was alone in the world.

Whereas Flora always felt that Miladin treated her as a heaven-sent diversion from the grim realities of warfare, Milosh always suspected her as a threat to the lawful occupation of soldiering. She could understand him. How could a Sergeant-Major not be astonished when a new recruit chatted casually with officers and obviously knew more about the state of the outside world than he did? He ate, breathed and lived by military regulations; he was not prepared to admit the existence of any other code. An Englishwoman in his company! It was enough to make any self-respecting Sergeant-Major take to drink!

Miladin thrived on human contacts; Milosh shunned them. Miladin could, if necessary, walk straight over to the Bulgar lines and make friends with half a dozen of them. Milosh had no such belief in the goodness of his fellow-men; he was his own man, and his only ally was military regulations.

Flora decided that their moustaches reflected the difference in their characters. Milosh's was invariably stiff and glossy, which Miladin swore was achieved by a mixture of sheep's fat and boot polish that Milosh hoarded, and that it was very good to eat smeared on bread. When questioned, Milosh merely scowled, muttered and refused to be drawn. He was very proud of his moustache.

Miladin's whiskers were quite different. Usually they lay draped across his upper lip like a skein of soft, black silk. When he was lost in thought, he would twirl one end round and round into the shape of a corkscrew. As often as not he would forget to untwirl it again. On several occasions Flora had seen him scramble to attention on the approach of Lieutenant Jovitch. Jovitch would stare at him curiously for a second or two and say, 'All right, you can stand at ease, Sergeant. And so can the left-hand side of your moustache.'

Miladin was thirty-three years old, the second son of a prosperous peasant farmer; he had a small farm of his own, a wife and two children. He had seen little of them since the first Turkish war of 1912, and Flora came to know that far-away look in his eyes. He missed his family but did not worry too much about their safety, for he had an unshakeable belief in the goodness of God.

A circle of men was now forming round the fire, linking arms for the Serbian national dance, the *kola*. From the smoky darkness a man appeared, seized her hand and dragged her from her seat. It was Janachko Jovitch, gay and laughing, his tunic open at the neck. He linked arms, pulled her into the circle, and, as the violins began to throb and voices began to sing, off they went, jigging round in time to the melodic folk tune. Flora had danced the *kola* many times before at the hospitals, but never like this. They circled and bobbed round the crackling flames, the ground churning to soft mud beneath their feet, minds freed for a moment from the shackles of war, no longer screwed to a tension pitch. It was a release and a reaffirmation. Tomorrow danger might return, but tonight the stars were high, they were free, and life was once again worth living.

Flora glanced up at Jovitch. He was singing happily. He caught her eye and, almost unbelievably, winked! He was completely altered, he looked young and carefree, his eyes were bright, and all the deeply etched lines in his face were smoothed into creases of laughter. Without thinking, she drew his arm closer to hers and held it warmly against her side.

The party went on until dawn. Flora delighted the company by borrowing a violin and playing 'God Save the King'. Her efforts to teach her *decetar* the words were less successful. Mirko laughed so much he fell backwards off his log into the mud.

The next morning she went to see Lieutenant Jovitch. She came straight to the point. When she said she imagined that the celebration dinner last night had pretty well emptied the company's food stocks, he nodded and admitted that except for a tiny reserve of bread there was nothing left. The men still had a few corn-cobs between them.

She explained her plan. Once they set off on their final march to the coast they were hardly likely to stop until they arrived. It might take between five and seven days. Couldn't they rake up some sort of meal for the company before they left? They had treated her to a wonderful party last night and she was anxious to do something in return. She could not feed the entire Serbian Army, not even the 2nd Regiment, but surely she could do something special for the 4th?

She had over a thousand cigarettes left in her baggage; that would mean about five cigarettes per man, and she also had one hundred and eighty French francs. The black market price in Elbasan was sixteen French francs a loaf, but, if she rode into the town and did some hard bargaining, perhaps she could find a sack of flour.

He stared back at her, said nothing but pulled back the flap of his tent and went inside. For a second Flora felt doubtful and hurt. At last he reappeared with a shabby little wallet, with the edges of a few faded photographs sticking out of it. He fumbled in one of the pockets and extracted a twenty-franc French note. It was all he had. Perhaps with two hundred francs they would be able to buy something. He would ride into the town with her.

As they rode into Elbasan Flora felt that things were different between them. Perhaps it was the party, perhaps he was getting more used to her; perhaps it was something to do with that grubby twenty-franc French note.

Flora disliked Elbasan. Its narrow uncobbled streets were deep in mud. The ill-washed townspeople stared at them distrustfully. A long procession of refugees, soldiers and Austrian prisoners of war had passed through this town in the past few months, and the inhabitants had turned indifferent faces towards all pleas for help. Oh, yes, they had been willing to barter a crust of bread for a warm overcoat or a pair of boots, which many of the people in the streets were now wearing.

They located the bakery and opened the door. A bell jangled above their heads. The cellar—it was no more than that—was dark, with a counter at one end. Behind it stood the baker, a small grimy man in a fur cap and a jacket buttoned up to his neck. His face was almost completely covered with brown fungus, from which his nose protruded like a small white cone. His black, beady eyes flickered from Lieutenant Jovitch's uniform to Flora's face. '*Bitte?*' he asked in German.

'Flour,' she said uncompromisingly. 'We want flour and none of your sixteen French francs a loaf!'

'There is no flour in Elbasan,' said the baker sourly.

'There must be flour. The townspeople eat.'

'They eat corn!'

'A bag of corn, then.'

The baker hesitated. 'A bag of corn meal will cost five hundred French francs.'

'Damn robber,' she said in English, before continuing in German. She rested her hand on the butt of her revolver and watched his eyes slide down to it.

'One hundred French francs.'

'Three hundred,' retorted the man.

'A hundred and fifty and we will see what size of a sack it is,' said Flora coldly.

'Two hundred, and the money first,' said the baker, aware of his strong position.

They loaded the sack of corn on the back of Jovitch's horse and, before setting off back to camp, called at Colonel Militch's headquarters. Flora waited outside for Jovitch.

When he returned, his face was grim. 'We march tomorrow,' he announced. On the way back to camp he said quietly, 'I didn't think you would get that corn.' He said it in a way which made her glow. He had never made a pleasant remark to her before.

She gave a short laugh. 'I was almost prepared to shoot him if I didn't.' And she almost meant it.

Back in camp, they handed the corn meal over to the Company cook with orders to make enough flat, round loaves to go round, half a loaf for each man.

Next morning the men of 4th Company paraded for their half-loaf and five cigarettes, and Lieutenant Jovitch made a crisp speech, saying it was a gift from England presented by Private Sandes.

When she rejoined them, Flora saw the eyes of the men in her *decetar* glowing with pride. Their mouths were too full of corn bread to thank her, but the look in their eyes was enough.

Before they left, the company paraded for prayers, led by the regimental priest from Elbasan. He set up his altar on a boulder, in the shelter of a high wall of rock. It was very simple: a white cloth spread out, a brass cross, and two candlesticks. Tall and black-bearded, in his high hat and flowing robes, the priest blessed the kneeling men and made the sign of the cross above their heads. The candle flames wavered in the breeze, the prayers echoed off the face of the rock and rang in Flora's ears. She watched Jovitch out of one eye. His eyes were closed and his lips moved noiselessly. Although a parson's daughter brought up in the Christian church, she wished that she could believe with such intensity.

There was no mistaking the route to the coast. They were the rearguard, and the thousands who had gone before had plainly marked the trail. It led up to the snowy crests of steep and barren mountains and down again to swampy valleys where you dragged your feet through deep mud. You could not lose your way. There were too many corpses for that: the bodies of men and women and children, the bloated corpses of oxen and horses, a never-ending trail of human and animal remains trodden into the snow and slush. You marched or you died.

They started each day at 4 or 5 a.m. and stopped to camp for the night between 6 and 7 p.m. in darkness, long after the short winter afternoon had ended. They halted every two hours for a fifteen-minute rest and, as soon as the whistle sounded, every man would slump down in his tracks and sleep in the mud or snow. When Jovitch shouted the order to move, the company would struggle to its feet, and the slow, weary procession would continue. Sometimes the sun in the valleys was hot and they gasped for breath. Sometimes the wind blew the snow off the mountains and froze their bones. At night, round the camp fires, the regiment gathered and talked in low, tired voices. They yearned to sleep, but first they talked of the old times, remembering good things and good places, summoning up strength enough from these memories to see them through the night and into the cold dawn mists, still hungry, still desperately tired, but prepared to go on.

Four nights after leaving Elbasan they camped among some holly bushes on a hillside. Many of the 4th Company were now exhausted and nearing starvation. Before setting up camp Jovitch had thrust a piece of bread about four inches square into her hand and told her to eat it for her supper. Like a child, she did as she was told.

Looking for him a little later, she rounded a holly bush to find him kneeling by the side of his own orderly who was propped up with his back against a tree trunk. For a second Flora could not make out what he was doing. He was breaking small pieces of bread from a crust and popping them into the orderly's mouth. She heard him say, 'You are eating this because I order you to. Do you understand?'

He glanced up guiltily at Flora, but passed it off by saying that these young men couldn't stand the pace, and that only the old soldiers could go on for ever.

A few yards away she almost stumbled over a large awkward-looking lump, covered by a large cape. She lifted one edge. Miladin and Milosh sat there, back to back, heads slumped forward, fast asleep. Both opened their eyes as she revealed them. Milosh growled and went straight back to sleep. Miladin smiled blissfully and did the same.

Within a few moments Jovitch arrived. She knew he would come, because it helped them both to talk. He sat down beside her on the dried holly leaves, which crackled under his weight. He sighed and rubbed his hand over his unshaven chin. 'Another day,' he said, 'another few miles closer.' During those days and nights she learnt as much about Janachko Jovitch as most women ever know about a single man in the whole of a lifetime.

He came from Belgrade. His father had died when he was very young, and his mother, a schoolteacher, had brought him up. They had been desperately poor; she had taught him as best she could, but she could only afford an elementary education, and he had left school early to work in a newspaper office. He liked the job because it dealt with events, with people, and with the turbulent politics of the Balkan peoples and their burning desire for freedom.

When the army, infuriated at the inhuman treatment of their brother Slavs in Macedonia, had marched against the Turks, and together with the Greeks and Bulgarians driven them from the remnants of their Balkan empire, an office desk could hold him no longer. Private Janachko Jovitch had gone off to the war. He had not been home since.

Like so many young people in Serbia, like Gavrilo Princep and the others who had plotted to assassinate the Archduke Ferdinand and were now rotting in Bosnian gaols, he was obsessed with the Slavonic dream. In the Middle Ages the Slavs had possessed an empire which embraced the entire Balkan peninsula except for southern Greece. The medieval glories of St Sava, Stephen Dushan and King Marko were as vivid and important to them as the sun in the sky. He tried to explain it to her: how the dream had lived in their hearts for a thousand years: a union of all the Slavonic people throughout the Balkans; a place where Bosnian, Croatian, Serbian, Macedonian, Montenegrin, Herzgovinian and Dalmatian could forget their enmities and unite in a country of their own. Serbia was defeated, but she had powerful allies and would rise again phoenix-like. They would live to fight again. Had they not retreated from the outskirts of Belgrade to the Baboona Pass fighting every step of the way?

At Baboona five thousand men, all that was left of the Moravian Division of which the 2nd Regiment was part, had faced twenty thousand Bulgars, held them at bay and even defeated them. When the 14th and 2nd Regiments had been left to cover the retreat, the enemy had flooded through the defile which carried the actual road through the pass. The Serbs had fired every round they had until the Bulgars had choked the narrow passage with their dead. But still they came. The Serbs had risen up from their rocks and hollows in the ground, surging forward, in a great mob. They had clashed, grappling with knives, bayonets, feet, teeth and nails, kicking, stabbing and scratching fanatically. The noise of men screaming and dying was a sound Jovitch would never forget.

Suddenly the Bulgars had turned and fled in wild panic.

It was a victory which had not lasted; it could not last. They had no reserves of men or ammunition; they could do nothing but return to their defensive posts and wait for the next order to retreat. Flora listened and marvelled. She remembered that not

A short halt on the mountains during the pursuit of the Bulgars

A wounded Serbian private welcomed back to his village

Captured Bulgars on their way to prison camp

The end of the campaign. Veteran soldiers of the Second Regiment on the homeward march

so far to the south lay a Greek pass called Thermopylae, which three hundred men, under a Spartan King, Leonidas, had held against the mighty Persian army of Xerxes. Their fame had lasted for more than fourteen hundred years. Would the same be true of Lieutenant Janachko Jovitch and the men who had defended the pass of Baboona with equal gallantry?

She crawled into the narrow grave-like trench which Dragutin had scraped out for her under a holly-bush. Jovitch stretched out where he was, pillowing his head on his arm. Flora snuggled down arranging her coat collar so that it protected her face from scratches. She wondered what her father would think of her now. Her headmistress at the school in Geneva would undoubtedly throw a fit. 'Young ladies will appear in the morning freshly bathed and in clean linen; their fingernails will be scrubbed and clipped short. . . .' Flora thought ruefully of her own dark-rimmed nails. Yet she wouldn't have had it any other way.

'We *old* soldiers,' Jovitch had said; and it was true. He was old before his time, desperate before his time, and yet she knew that he, too, would not have had it any different. She did not then know that a new generation of poets and writers would rise from the terrible carnage of the war and reveal it in all its futility. No one knew, and, had they known, they could have done nothing about it. They were committed. They were people apart, hardly people at all, merely soldiers. Civilians lived in a different world fatly encompassed by things beyond the hope or the grasp of any soldier. Amidst the corruption of dirt and death there was a monastic purity about their motive, a wind-scoured, bone-scraped edge to their lives which repaid them in some measure for all they gave up.

They set off again at five before the sun had risen, and now, as they trudged along, Flora remarked that the mountains were not quite so high or so bleak as before. Jovitch, walking beside her, also leading his horse, nodded agreement. His face was grim. The entire company had now been practically without food for five days. Unless they got some help by night, some of his men would never finish the journey. He told her this, and to ease his deep anxiety she began to talk about the sea. The sea should be quite close now, she insisted. They would be able to smell it soon. Even in December or January the Adriatic should be quite blue.

Two hours later they noticed some excitement in the 1st Company marching ahead. They were quite close before they realised why. Three men in strange uniforms were standing among them. They were officers from the Italian Military Mission in Durazzo who had walked out to meet them. It was still a very long march to Kavajë, a few miles from Durazzo, but a camp had been prepared for them there and there was food waiting. If they could reach Kavajë, they were safe.

The news spread through the ranks. Faces lightened, backs straightened. Jovitch gathered the Company round him and said grimly that they would march as they had never marched before. He knew that most of them were near to exhaustion, but that the 4th Company had never failed him yet. They would rest for five minutes every hour, but they were going to march on and on until they reached the camp at Kavajë.

Like men in a dream, pale and footsore, they set off again. At dusk they reached Kavajë, and the inhabitants turned out, not to cheer them, but merely to watch the long, shambling column of exhausted, gaunt and dispirited men staggering through. Flora had never seen anything like the mud in that town. It flowed between the houses like a slimy river into which men plunged knee-deep. She dismounted. Her horse would never carry her through it. Every few yards even in the town itself the bodies of dead horses stuck out of the slime.

Once outside Kavajë they could see the camp fires of the 2nd Regiment, which had arrived first. They twinkled on the hillside about two miles farther on. She found herself weeping with sheer frustration. At each step her feet sank so far in that the mud covered the tops of her boots. The stench from the dead horses was appalling. It took her three hours to cover the comparatively short distance. Utterly exhausted, she slumped on the hillside as Dragutin fixed her tent. Usually she helped him, but now she was too tired even to move.

She said wearily, 'Well, we're here. Tomorrow there's bound to be food for us.'

In the light of a neighbouring fire she saw his sad eyes turn towards her.

'Yes,' he said sombrely. Flora had never seen him quite so low. They were safe, she repeated. What was the matter with him?

She heard him sigh, and then he told her thoughtfully and without animosity, so that she should know that he was not complaining but merely stating a fact, that she had ridden some of the way, but he had walked all the way; perhaps she would have something to eat presently but he would have nothing.

Flora sat there on the damp cold hillside and felt ashamed. Every evening for the past five days Jovitch had handed her a small piece of bread. She had eaten it because she was hungry and because he had told her to. She doubted if Jovitch had eaten anything at all.

Three hours earlier, before they reached Kavajë, he had given her the usual small crust of dark rye bread. She had put it in her pocket knowing it was there to eat whenever she wanted it. Somehow, it helped her to carry on. Now she had to give it up. Your men are always your concern, Jovitch had told her a few nights earlier, and now she knew that Dragutin was her concern.

She called him across, fished in her pocket and held out the piece of bread. His dark conspirator's eyes stared down as if it was a glittering diamond bracelet. In the faint light Flora could see how thin and haggard his face had become. His lips moved and he tried to say something. He shook his head.

Flora pushed it into his hand. She was not hungry, she lied, she was too tired to eat. He turned the bread over and over in his dirty hand.

'Go away and eat it,' said Flora. 'I'm going to sleep.'

She crawled into her tent. She realised then that it was New Year's Eve. For a moment, she wondered what her friends and relatives would be doing in England. Would people be waving rattles and wearing funny hats and kissing under the mistletoe? Oh well, let them! As far as she was concerned the only way of celebrating just then was to curl up and sleep and sleep and sleep.

Chapter Six

I

FLORA ALWAYS remembered the ten miles to Durazzo, the chief port on the Albanian coast, for two reasons : the wrecks along the shore and the dead horses along the roadside. No one had had the time or energy to bury the dead horses and the stench was revolting when the wind blew the wrong way.

From the top of the hill behind their camp, they looked out across low sand dunes to the blue and sparkling Adriatic. Beyond, a long curving rib of golden sand stretched round to Durazzo, a jumble of roofs and walls and dockside cranes. Along this beach, protruding from the shoals, lay the blackened hulls and spars of many wrecks; torpedoed by Austrian submarines or struck by floating mines, most of them had sunk trying to beach through the shallow water.

By eight o'clock in the morning Italian lorries were unloading cases of bully beef and sacks of flour at the camp. Within minutes the regimental cooks were baking bread and opening cans, and the hungry soldiers had formed queues and were waiting for their rations. By noon everyone had been fed, and the band, which had stuck to its instruments right across the mountains, was playing regimental airs.

Within a week they had made the camp comfortable. Flora managed to get some sugar through the British Adriatic Mission, for British and Italian units had already arrived by sea to give aid. They had already been given coffee, and for one whole afternoon the members of 4th Company sat round their fires drinking small highly-sweetened cups of black Turkish coffee.

She was also given a small green bivouac tent by the Mission, and with Miladin and Dragutin's help, dug a hole three feet deep and piled the earth into a circular parapet; then she pitched the tent on top of the parapet and built an earth fireplace at one end, with a hole for the smoke to escape. All the equipment she had brought from England had disappeared in the retreat: her camp bed, her portable rubber bath and small medicine-chest, although she still had a few precious aspirin and quinine tablets. However, she soon made her tent quite snug: she laid down a bed of spruce boughs and used bully-beef boxes for chairs and tables.

A week after they arrived in Durazzo Jovitch called her into his tent and told her the good news. In view of her services to the Company and her general ability, he was promoting her to corporal. This would be entered in the Company records and into her pay-book.

Mirko invited her to his tent to celebrate over a cup of coffee with a few friends. This, he said, was a great day. With Flora as corporal, the affairs of the Company *must* prosper; indeed, if the news reached the enemy, they would probably retreat straightaway to Sofia!

A few days later she almost lost her promotion.

An officer from another battalion invited her to lunch at his camp several miles away, which meant starting early in the morning. She went to find Jovitch but he was nowhere to be seen, so she left without asking permission.

She was so warmly received by the other company that she stayed not only for lunch but for dinner, and it was past midnight when she got back to camp. Next morning Dragutin opened the flap of her tent and told her grimly that the Company Commander wanted to see her at once.

Janachko Jovitch was wearing what she called his 'military expression'. He ordered her to follow him, led her briskly to the outskirts of the camp and pointed up the hillside.

Fifty yards away one of the sergeants was drilling a single unhappy private, heavily lumbered with overcoat, blanket, cape, full equipment and rifle. He was doubling, marking time, about turning and perspiring freely as he underwent four hours' punishment drill in the hot sunshine. Four hours' punishment drill was the normal sentence when a soldier disobeyed an order, Jovitch said curtly. She had no right to leave camp without permission; it was absence without leave, an offence punishable by military law. If she wanted to stay with the 4th Company, she must realise at once that she was not going to be shown any favours.

'Yes, sir,' said Flora meekly.

This time, he said, he would simply reprimand her, but should she repeat the offence, it would mean either punishment drill or not less than five days' confinement to camp.

'Yes, sir,' she said, the colour rising in her cheeks. She marched back to her tent feeling very sorry for herself, but was once again intercepted by Mirko. He had some hot coffee ready, gave her the best seat in his tent, placed a small cup in her hand, and commiserated. There were many things about the army which her Uncle Mirko would have to teach her. If he, Mirko, had been punished for all the misdemeanours he had committed, he would have been shot at dawn years ago. You had to learn to use guile, to weave your way through the gaps left in the fence of military regulations. With Uncle Mirko's tuition she should be able to get along all right.

Flora thought Mirko wonderful. He had the sort of face to be found in every bazaar between Bagdad and Salonika; his small round nose protruded from his fat cheeks, and his nostrils curved down to full and sensuous lips above a blue and rounded jowl. The way he circumvented trouble was fantastic. Flora once saw him, with the bound feet of a stolen goose sticking out of his haversack, accosted by a young officer from another regiment. What was that bird doing in his haversack? Did he not know the penalty for looting?

Looting! Every curve of Mirko's face quivered with horror. The officer must realise that a generous nature like his could not stand the thought of a poor creature with a damaged wing trying to fly. After much difficulty he had captured it, tied it to prevent it hurting itself and was about to deliver it to the veterinary surgeon in the next town. He had been protecting bird life ever since he was a small child . . . Surely, the Lieutenant knew that this was quite a rare species of goose. The young officer had snorted and ridden on leaving Mirko grinning after him. And Flora realised there were things you had to learn about being a soldier which were not printed in the manuals.

Still, she was angry at having left herself open to Jovitch's lecture. The last thing she wanted to have was direct access to the Colonel or any similar privilege. She merely wanted to be an ordinary member of the 4th Company.

However, being a woman, she could not help being amused when two mornings later Dragutin woke her up to tell her that the Lieutenant was ill and needed her.

In his tent, under a rumpled pile of blankets, Jovitch was flushed and feverish. 'Ah, Corporal Sandes,' he said weakly, 'I shall get up in a minute.'

Flora took his temperature and felt his pulse. 'You will do nothing of the sort, Lieutenant Jovitch,' she said severely. She examined the thermometer and smiled. It was over 100. There was nothing for it: she would have to revert to her original job of nurse. Blandly she told him that unless he wanted four hours' punishment drill or not less than five days' confinement to camp, he would have to obey her orders. He would stay in bed, take the tablets she gave him, and live entirely on soups and liquids. He was not to get up until his temperature was gone, and, if he disobeyed her, she would call in the Regimental Doctor. That would probably mean going to hospital for other things, such as—the extraction of a bullet.

Weakly he agreed, too sick to do otherwise. Flora gave instructions to his orderly, and for the next five days dosed him on aspirin and quinine tablets. It was not revenge, because she knew how quickly any illness could turn into pneumonia. Jovitch, however, did not see it that way. When, for the third day in succession, he both lunched and dined on watery soup, he peered from his blankets and accused her of only doing it to pay him out.

She examined the thermometer critically. 'You should be able to get up for a little while tomorrow,' she said. 'And don't be childish, Lieutenant. You've been very ill.'

Next morning she was surprised to receive a visitor; a private from the British Adriatic Mission bringing a message from, of all people, Miss Simmonds. She was staying at the hotel in Durazzo and had been told by the Mission that Flora was there. They had to meet at once.

Holding the note, she entered Lieutenant Jovitch's tent and was surprised to find him seated on his bed, eating a large plate of stew.

'Ah, Corporal,' he said cheerfully, 'thanks to your nursing I am now quite well again.' He speared a piece of mutton with his fork and popped it into his mouth.

'In that case,' she said, 'I would like to request leave of absence to visit my friend, Miss Simmonds, who has unexpectedly arrived here.'

He put down his plate. In their long discussions during the

retreat she had told him all about Simmo. 'Very well, Corporal,' he said, 'as a small token of thanks for your work in nursing the sick you are given three days' leave. And if you want a horse, you can borrow mine.'

Miss Simmonds was not at the hotel, but had left a message to say she was calling on Crown Prince Alexander at his house on the outskirts of Durazzo. Would Flora join her there?

Leaving her horse at the hotel, she walked to the house. Two armed sentries were posted at the gates and a Serbian flag was flying from the flag-pole in the garden. The sentries, seeing her uniform, saluted respectfully and let her pass. In the large entrance hall a young officer rose from his desk and said he would take her in to see the Crown Prince at once. He led her through into a large comfortable lounge where Miss Simmonds leapt up from a chair, gave her a great hug demanding what had she been up to and why was she so skinny, her hair turning white, and what was she doing in that soldier's uniform when she was supposed to be a nurse?

The aide-de-camp coughed discreetly, and Flora excused herself and turned to be presented to the Crown Prince. He was younger than she expected: a slight, dark young man with a thin, intelligent face and a pencil-line moustache. He shook her hand, said he was very pleased to make her acquaintance and could not thank them both adequately for what they had done for his country. Flora had heard much about Alexander. As a child in Geneva he had experienced extreme poverty. His father, the present King Peter, had lived there in exile before being recalled to the throne of Serbia. Alexander's first school was an elementary one, but later the Tzar of Russia had taken over his education and that of his two brothers, and he had gone to the Military Academy in St Petersburg. Then his elder brother was judged to be insane, and at this very moment King Peter, old and infirm, was delegating his authority and all his responsibilities to Alexander.

During his stay at St Petersburg Alexander had fallen deeply in love with one of the Tzar's daughters. The Serbian Prime Minister made tentative inquiries at the Romanoff Court on his behalf, but the bad luck attached to Alexander Karageorgevitch was already beginning. Within two years the girl he loved was to be brutally murdered with the Tzar and the rest of her family, shot to death by the Bolsheviks in a cellar in Ekaterinburg.

No one could foresee either that Alexander, after the war, would never prove dynamic or statesman enough to reconcile the conflicting demands of Croat, Serb and Slovene, or even understand the radical forces at work in his own country. Despite his liberal upbringing, he was to be forced to establish a military dictatorship in Yugoslavia. And when on 9 October 1934 high drama and bad luck coincided, Alexander Karageorgevitch, King of Yugoslavia, riding in a carriage up the Canebière in Marseilles, died with an assassin's bullet in his breast. But all this tragedy was yet to come.

Now the aide-de-camp reappeared carrying two small leather cases. Each contained a Sveti Sava medal. The Crown Prince had great pleasure in presenting one to both Miss Simmonds and Flora in recognition of their services to Serbia.

Both girls were astonished and delighted. Afterwards, back in the hotel, they eagerly exchanged news. Simmo explained that there were refugees everywhere: thousands in Salonika, Scutari and even here in Durazzo. She had already made three boat-trips with the homeless to reception camps in Corsica, Corfu and Marseilles; she was leaving at midnight with yet another boatload for Corsica.

All her humanitarian instincts aroused, she cross-examined Flora relentlessly. Did she really like being a soldier? Did she intend to march back with the Serbian Army on their return? Did she understand that in a war soldiers are not only killed but have to kill? Did Flora really understand that with all the romantic nonsense ripped away, that is what she would be—a killer!

'Yes,' said Flora, 'I do.'

Miss Simmonds's voice rose a little. This wasn't Flora's sort of work. She was a nurse, a woman. Her job was to save life, not to take it. Why didn't she stop playing at soldiers and come with her that very night on the boat to Corsica?

Flora smiled sadly. Even if she told her old friend all about Jovitch, Vukoye and Doditch, Mirko, Miladin and Dragutin, the times they had spent together and the miseries they had shared, she knew Simmo would never understand. How could she explain that in this one small group of ordinary soldiers, she had found the answer to all she had sought?

All this, without much success, she tried to tell Simmo in halting sentences. At midnight she stood on the quayside in the darkness watching the ship slide away from the dock, knowing that Simmo would never understand, but would not love her any the less because of it. Her high, clear voice floated down, 'Take care of yourself, Flora. God bless!'

She watched the bright wake of foam phosphorescent behind the ship. She heard its siren moan three times. Blacked out because of submarines it disappeared swiftly into the night and she was left alone. Suddenly it was cold. She turned on her heel, glad to be starting back to camp.

II

The battle for survival really began when they were moved from Durazzo to the Greek island of Corfu. They expected sunshine, olive groves, blue seas, fruit and wine; yet for the first six weeks it rained incessantly, the blue seas were the colour of tarpaulin, and the olive groves inches deep in mud.

At 3 a.m. on a cold wet morning she and sixty men of the 4th Company under Lieutenant Jovitch disembarked at a small quay miles from the city. They discovered that their tents, blankets and kit were not on the same ship and no one had any knowledge of where or when they were likely to reappear.

The Italian sailors bundled them ashore with great courtesy and maximum speed. No one was there to meet them, and they did not know in which direction their camp lay. Some distant brass-hat had made the decision to embark part of the 2nd Regiment from Durazzo and part from Valona, another Albanian port a little farther down the coast, and land them at Corfu, and had then promptly forgotten all about them.

Flora and Jovitch spent the rest of the night sitting on packing-cases in front of a sentry's fire and cursing brass-hats. At seven o'clock a Serbian officer appeared and informed them that their company was to camp upon a hillside some eight miles away and he would be grateful if they would march there at once.

By this time the ship containing their equipment had arrived. By this time too it was pouring with rain, and various unpleasant facts had come to light. There was no hay for bedding, no timber for fires, and no rations of any sort whatever. No bread, no bully beef, no flour and no likelihood of any arriving.

Late that afternoon, accompanied by their orderlies, they went in search of supplies. At a village four miles away they discovered a baker who had bread. He was willing to change their Serbian money, and they bought some at a very poor rate of exchange, at three francs a loaf, twenty-two loaves in all, giving each man a third of a loaf.

They went back to their cold, wet camp, chewed soggy bread and shivered for the rest of the night.

The next morning Lieutenant Jovitch and Flora stood in the rain, staring down the muddy track which led towards Corfu some fifteen miles away. No rations or liaison officer had shown up. A few seabirds floated overhead from time to time, hooted derisively and rapidly turned back towards the ocean. A cold wind blew gusts of rain in their faces.

Suddenly, from far off, came the dull roar of a lorry but when it came into sight they saw it was taking wood into Corfu.

It was at this moment that the idea struck her that she might get a lift and go into Corfu. She could at least remind the brass-hats of their presence. Remembering her success in Elbasan, Jovitch gave permission and wished her luck.

Flora raced down the hill and waved wildly, until the lorry ground to a stop. A cheerful red face craned down from a British khaki uniform.

As they jolted along the road, Flora thought over the events of the past few weeks. Most of her experiences had been harrowing but one in particular had been very pleasant. The red-letter day when she was officially sworn into the Serbian Army . . .

The Regiment had formed into a square. In the centre stood a table on which was laid a bowl of water, a bunch of leaves, a large brass cross and a Serbian Bible. The recruits had paraded near the table with the officers in front of them. The band played and the Regimental colours were blessed by a priest. The recruits were called to attention. The sacred oath was read out to them as they stood at the salute, and repeated it word for word. They swore allegiance and loyalty to Serbia and King Peter. Afterwards they marched past the table, pausing to let the priest sprinkle their foreheads with water while they kissed first the cross and then the regimental flag.

In the city, the lorry-driver dropped her off outside the British Mission and wished her luck.

She climbed the steps to the front door. A military policeman inside listened politely while she explained her mission and, after waiting half an hour, she was shown into a small office occupied by a young Lieutenant who said he would arrange for her to see the Major.

After another half-hour, she was shown into the Major's office. He was small, dapper and brusque to the point of rudeness. They were doing all they could. His small organisation was working around the clock, but what could you expect but chaos when a defeated army was thrown ashore on a small island like Corfu with insufficient preparation? His advice was to return to her unit and wait. The Serbian authorities would sort it all out.

In the outer office, the young Lieutenant looked up sympathetically.

'Any luck?'

'No, I'm supposed to go round to Serbian Headquarters.'

He scrutinised her carefully. 'Are your chaps really without food?' he said.

'We've spent all our own money buying bread,' said Flora. 'We've only got a few francs left, not enough to buy bread for all the men.'

The young man cleared his throat and fished a wallet out of his breast-pocket. He produced a hundred-franc note. 'Would you think it impertinent?' he ventured.

She smiled. She would borrow it gladly and pay it back at the first opportunity.

At the Serbian Headquarters they were pleasant but unhelpful. The French were in charge of most of the food on the island; she should try them.

It was still raining when she went out into the streets again. The cold wind froze her, but she still had the hundred francs. She asked the way to the largest bakery in town. The baker was pleasant. Yes, he had plenty of loaves; he could sell her a couple. She wanted a hundred francs' worth? Oh no, that was quite impossible! That would mean a signed authorization from the military authorities.

Wearily she dragged herself around to the French military headquarters for another long wait. At long last she was shown in to a Colonel. He was tall, had a bristly white moustache and a very crisp manner. The fact that a Serbian corporal—and a most peculiar English female one at that—had had the impertinence to appear in his office demanding rations did not amuse him one bit.

Officers of the rank of captain and above had to sign such requests, he said. No doubt the requirements of her company would be met in due course; but there were other regiments to be served as well as hers. Flora asked quietly if at least he would sign an authorization for her to buy bread. No, he would not. Good afternoon!

A third door banged in her ear and Flora was out in the rain again. She took a deep breath, thrust out her lower lip, marched back to British headquarters, pushed almost rudely past the red-cap on duty and bearded the Major. He coldly repeated that he intended to do nothing.

The young Lieutenant looked at her face as she came out and then looked hastily away. He tapped the table with his pencil and stammered, 'Now look, old girl, why don't you come and have dinner with me in the Mess? You'll feel a lot better.'

It was very kind of him, but she could not accept. She could not eat until they all ate. She tried to explain to the Lieutenant, who nodded uncomfortably.

'Well, if I were you,' he said, 'I'd go straight back to the French. Damn it all, you're a woman. All this "*cherchez la femme*" stuff. Give 'em another go!'

Outside it was almost dark and still raining as she walked slowly back towards the French headquarters. The Lieutenant was right. The Colonel was her last chance.

She was kept waiting for fifteen minutes before being shown into his office again.

His pale blue eyes opened wide in annoyance when they saw her; had he not already made it quite clear that all Serbian units would be fed and clothed in due course? Had he not made it quite clear—

Flora took another deep breath. She was soaked to the skin, she was hungry and she was miserable. She had walked about all day in the rain from office to office, and she had fifteen miles to walk back to camp, and no one had taken the slightest notice of her. She could almost anticipate the look in Jovitch's eyes. He would try and hide his disappointment; but it wouldn't be any good.

Didn't he realize, she asked desperately, that they had lived on scraps of bread and a few mealie cobs for months and months and months? They'd fought the Germans and they'd fought the Austrians and they'd fought the Bulgarians, and they'd fight them all again if they got the chance. They had crossed the mountains, walking every inch of the way. And now they'd all die of starvation when they were supposed to be safe.

Just then, to her utter confusion, tears welled up into her eyes. She blinked rapidly, trying to check them, but they kept on rolling down her cheeks. She blinked even more vigorously and at last had to rub her cheeks with her knuckles. Only silly women cried, she told herself, but it was no use. She buried her face in her hands and her shoulders heaved. At any second she expected to hear the Colonel order her out of his office, but she didn't care any more. She was a failure. The whole of the 4th Company would starve to death on their hillside and it would be her fault.

To her intense surprise she felt a man's arm around her shoulders, and a soft voice telling her not to distress herself. Through the gaps in her fingers, Flora saw the Colonel's large white linen handkerchief dangling in front of her. She grabbed it at once and blew her nose vigorously, trying to apologise.

The Colonel patted her shoulders. She must dry her eyes while he sent for coffee and cognac. He had been far too short with her, and it was quite admirable that she should be so concerned for her company. While they drank their coffee, he would send out his orderly to secure a carriage and would personally order enough bread and bully-beef for sixty men from the commissariat, which she could take back with her. Tomorrow he would personally see to it that they were on the official supply-list.

With the loaves to one side, the cases of bully-beef under her feet and the brandy still warm in her stomach, Flora enjoyed her drive back to camp. She stopped at a wine-merchant to spend some of the hundred francs on a large barrel of wine, and drove on again. The sentry heard the carriage long before she arrived, and sixty men with Lieutenant Jovitch were all waiting at the bottom of the hill when her driver reined to a halt. She was handed out of the carriage by Jovitch as if she had been a queen paying a formal visit.

Next morning Jovitch called her into his tent and Flora pointed out that if they did not look after themselves, nobody else would. From now on, she suggested, they should make their own survival a matter of primary importance. What did they need for a start?

'Wood for fires,' said Jovitch without hesitation. Without fires they couldn't have a hot meal or hot coffee; they couldn't even keep warm.

Flora nodded. She remembered that the lorry which had taken her into town had carried timber and was driven by a British Tommy who seemed a decent sort. She had a short consultation with Mirko. They discovered that lorries passed along the road at the bottom of their camp at fairly regular intervals.

With Mirko's help she set about making friends with the British Tommies. Strangely enough—unlike many of the British officers she met in Salonika later, who were quite certain she was some sort of 'camp follower'—the British Tommies accepted her status as a soldier without hesitation.

A few mornings later, by 'coincidence', several huge logs of wood fell off one of the lorries just beyond their camp. Within seconds they had been hauled up the hill and were lost to sight amongst the Serbian tents.

Flora was still not satisfied. The entire 2nd Regiment had now disembarked and were camped upon their hillside. The French Colonel had been as good as his word; rations of bread and bully-beef now arrived regularly, but Corfu and headquarters were fifteen miles away and that was too far for Flora.

The Serbian Relief Fund, whose chief task was to distribute the aid given by the French and British, were desperately short of help: they'd wanted Flora to work for them. Would Jovitch release her for a period? She was sure she could be more use to the 2nd Regiment in the middle of Corfu than stuck out here. Jovitch gave her his blessing.

From then on Flora Sandes attached herself to the Serbian Relief Fund and found lodgings in the town. Life for the 2nd Regiment improved appreciably. She was of great use to the Relief Fund because she spoke both French and German fluently, and Serbian with a zest that surprised everybody she met. All goods had to be ferried by lighter from ships lying off shore to warehouses on the quayside. Most of the labour was supplied by squads of Serbian soldiers seconded from their regiments. It was not unusual to find an Englishman who could not speak French trying to explain to a French official who couldn't speak English that he wanted a fatigue party of Serbian soldiers to unload a lighter and then both being quite unable to explain what they wanted, because neither spoke Serbian.

The Serbian Relief Fund submitted meekly, although Flora quickly discovered that there was little to be gained from merely working at their headquarters. Real power resided in the docks, with the gangs of soldiers unloading the ships.

She therefore made friends with an enormous North Country corporal, six foot four inches tall, who had been a stevedore in Liverpool before joining the Regular Army and was one of the very few with an expert knowledge of how to unload a ship. At first she was shy of approaching him. He was the real thing: a regular British N.C.O., and what was she? A woman Corporal, in his eyes probably no better than a music-hall turn. She dreaded what he might think but approached him hesitantly. He looked at her with his icy blue eyes and told her in a Durham accent, which she had almost as much difficulty in understanding as she once had Serbian, that she could count on him. To start with it would be a good idea if she worked down there on the Docks; he added. Half the time these Froggies and Eyeties and Greeks didn't understand a word he was saying!

Flora Sandes and her gang of stevedores quickly became a feature of the Corfu waterfront. The Serbian Army's lice-ridden, filthy uniforms had all been burnt, and replaced with thin blue overalls. Chill winter winds blew in from the sea, and unless they soon had extra clothes many of them would go down with colds and influenza.

Under the expert tuition of the corporal Flora found it quite simple to balance a large case of woollen sweaters in a precarious position and look surprised when it crashed to the floor. It was only commonsense that the sweaters should be worn immediately and not left around in the warehouse to get dirty.

Flora soon determined to equip the entire 2nd Regiment of over a thousand men. She did not regard this as dishonest. The clothing had been sent out to be worn, not kept in quartermaster's stores; she simply speeded up its distribution.

It was a matter of life and death. The Serbian Army, weakened to the point of extinction by suffering, hardship and malnutrition, were losing men at the rate of one hundred and fifty a day. An irregular diet of bully beef and bread, unsuitable clothes, apart from cold and wintry weather and home-sickness, had a cumulative effect which many could not withstand.

She visited the tiny island just off the coast of Corfu which had been turned into a hospital for the Serbians. A doctor showed her round. So many died each day that the corpses were carried out to sea by tug and buried there.

He told of one old man, a refugee, who had come to see his son, his last and youngest; the other six had been killed in the war. He was too late; his son had died the day before. 'He asked to see his grave,' explained the doctor quietly, 'and I knew that at that very moment his body was lying out on the quay waiting for the tug to arrive.' The doctor shrugged as if trying to unburden his conscience. 'What could I tell him? I knew the lad's body would have to be taken out with the others and buried at sea, and all Serbs hate the sea. I took him along and showed him one of the graves with a small wooden cross above it. These soldiers had been buried in the island because the sea was too rough for the tug to take the bodies out. I deceived the old man so that he would be able to tell his wife that he had seen the last resting-place of their son and give her some consolation.'

Flora was now determined to overcome the official lethargy she found everywhere. She knew that thousands of new uniforms had arrived and were being held in French custody. She made inquiries. The French were prepared to issue uniforms upon production of a proper authorization. But on one condition: that there were underclothes to go with them. As the French possessed no underclothes it was obviously impossible to issue uniforms! Flora soon discovered that the British possessed large stocks of underclothing and obtained an official document from the French, declaring they were prepared to issue uniforms on production of underclothes. From the Serbian Relief Fund she then procured a very formal-looking document, signed by every high-ranking officer she could find, requesting the British to release 3,500 sets of pants and vests. She went to the British Captain who was O.C. Stores. With a rather superior smile he said that of course they were perfectly prepared to part with these items once uniforms were issued, but as there were no uniforms there was nothing he could do about it.

She did not actually want them to part with 3,500 sets of pants and vests, retorted Flora sweetly. All she wanted was a document declaring that, if by some miracle of providence, 3,500 uniforms should turn up, then they were prepared to issue the underclothes to go with them.

As this seemed fairly safe, the O.C. Stores drafted an authorization. Flora pounced like a tigress. Armed with her three sets of papers, she set off for the headquarters of the Serbian Minister of War resident in Corfu. She made it plain to anyone who cared to listen that, come hell or high water, she was going to stay there until the Minister for War himself countersigned all three sets of papers.

It is perhaps difficult to understand why she was not court-martialled or at any rate reprimanded. Possibly because no member of the Serbian Army was held in greater esteem or affection by its senior officers and, had any member of the other Allied Forces dared to say a word against her, a riot would undoubtedly have broken out.

The Minister of War freely signed her authorizations. Flora ran back to the British and French authorities with a signature big enough to impress even a quartermaster-sergeant. Once proper military transport arrived, they would arrange to release the items in question. Flora had forgotten about transport. She interviewed the young British Lieutenant in charge of the motor pool. He frowned. It was no use her simply saying she wanted him to transport 3,500 uniforms and the same number of pants and vests. He had to know the exact weight and bulk of the articles.

Flora restrained herself, gathered up her papers and went back to confer with her corporal. He was unperturbed. This was normal military procedure. Nothing to it, really.

'But how,' demanded Flora in despair, 'can you possibly turn 3,500 vests, pants and uniforms of assorted sizes into so many cubic feet?'

'Now don't fret, lass,' said the corporal producing a stub of pencil and a torn envelope. These things had to go through 'the proper channels'. He winked. Flora stood gnawing her lip while he did a few sums. Within two minutes he had worked it all out.

It was a proud and smiling Corporal Sandes who finally halted her convoy of lorries outside the camp and superintended the unloading of the bales of clothing. She reported first to Lieutenant

Jovitch who personally escorted her to Colonel Militch. The Colonel was very pleased and congratulated her. Even Mirko was impressed. Obviously Corporal Sandes had benefited from his advice.

A week later she was called to a small meeting outside Jovitch's tent. A deputation had been formed, which included Vukoye and Doditch, Miladin and Sergeant-Major Milosh, Mirko, Dratza and a dozen others from the company.

Jovitch called them to attention and handed her two papers. One was in Serbian and the other in English.

He looked a little bashful. 'A translation,' he explained hesitantly, 'so that you can read it in your own language.' It had been difficult to find someone to translate it into English. The paper read:— 'To the high esteemed Miss Flora Sandes, Corfu. Esteemed Miss Sandes! Soldiers of the 4th Company, 1st Battalion, 2nd Infantry Regiment, Moravian Division, 1st Call Reserves; touched with your nobleness wish with this letter to pay their respects and thankfulness to you; have chosen a committee to hand you this letter of thankfulness.

'Miss Sandes! Serbian soldier is proud because in his midst he sees a noble daughter of England, whose people is an old Serbian friend, and today their armies are arm-in-arm fighting for common idea, and you Miss Sandes should be proud that you are in position to do a good to help a Serbian soldier; Serbian soldier will always respect acts of your kindness and deep down in his heart will write your kind acts and remember them for ever.

'Few months have passed since you came among us and you shared good and bad with us. During this time you have often helped us to pass through hardships, buying food for us and financially.

'Thanking you in the name of all the soldiers, we are greeting you with exclamation:

Long life to our Ally England,
Long life to Serbia,
Long life to their heroic armies,
Long life to noble Miss Sandes!'

Here followed the names of the committee the Company had chosen to present the letter, and it ended, 'Please receive this little, but from heart of my soldiers, declaration of thankfulness for all (for help) that you have done for them until now, and in time, when they are far away from dear ones and loving ones at home. To their wishes and declaration I am adding mine and exclaim: Long life to our dear ally England. Long life to heroic Serbian Army. Commander of the Company Janachko A. Jovitch.'

'The translation is all right?' asked Jovitch anxiously.

'It is perfect,' said Flora, much moved. 'Thank you all very much.'

After two months' stay the 2nd Regiment received its sailing-orders for Salonika, from where they would be launched back into the battle.

Their sailing-date was delayed for one day, however, so that the Regiment could celebrate its birthday—its 'Slava Day'.

The sun shone, the Regiment paraded in their new uniforms and the Crown Prince, the Commander of the 1st Army and all sorts of high ranking officers from the British and French forces arrived. The bands played; the marquees were decorated with flags.

Flora was chatting with Colonel Militch when suddenly he asked where her Company was drawn up. She told him they were over behind the 3rd.

'Come over here and stand beside me,' ordered Militch. 'I want to have a word with them.'

As they approached, the 4th Company sprang to attention, and Colonel Militch began a speech in a voice loud enough for not only the 4th to hear but most of the other Companies as well.

As they all knew, this was their Slava Day, but it was more than just another celebration. It was perhaps the most important Slava Day in the history of their Regiment. They had just survived a most disastrous retreat. Tomorrow they were sailing to Salonika and soon they would be back in battle to drive the enemy from their homeland.

He had decided to make a public announcement of what was usually no more than a slight change in the Company's books. A promotion! With immediate effect Corporal Sandes, whom they all knew and esteemed, was promoted to the rank of Sergeant.

Modestly she wrote home afterwards: 'They all shouted "*Jivio*" three times for me when he had finished and though I felt extremely shy and embarrassed, I was very much pleased.'

The old bear, Major Pesitch, C.O. of the 1st Battalion, insisted upon personally fastening the stars upon her shoulder. Even General Vassitch, Commander of the 1st Army, summoned her to congratulate her.

One last event remained in her memory. The bands played, the *kola* had been danced by British guests and French guests and hosts of Serbian soldiers. By four o'clock in the morning the party was dying and Flora was seated round a camp fire with Miladin and Mirko, Milosh, Dratza and Dragutin. Mirko, still sucking away at a pork bone, paused to wipe the grease from his mouth with the back of his hand and grin at her.

'Sandes,' he said happily, 'you're going to be such a lovely sergeant!'

Chapter Seven

I

IN THE middle of August the 2nd Regiment left Salonika for the front. They marched along the dusty roads to the railhead, columns of tall, lean, bronzed men, and Sergeant Flora Sandes was very proud to march in their ranks. They were off to the war, they were going to fight their way back into Serbia; they were going home.

The train chugged northwards across the undulating plain towards the mountains. The plains were green in places, divided into long strips, and the primitive ox-drawn ploughs cut long, dark brown furrows in the pale fawn wheat-stubble. Occasionally they saw the bright swathe of the Vardar in the sunshine, wide and smooth-flowing after its twisting race through the mountains.

Jolting northwards, Flora tried to rationalize her feelings. Was this slight dryness in her mouth fear, or simply the dust floating in the air? She knew that in a war the difference between an 'attack' and a 'retreat' was a dramatic one. In a retreat you fled ignominiously from the enemy and ran for your life, your main object self-preservation. In an attack you advanced grimly and determinedly into the enemy's fire: you grappled with him and destroyed him when he dared to resist.

When Vukoye shouted, 'Fix bayonets!' and she heard the cold, metallic sound of steel blades being slotted into bayonet fixing-rings, how would she act? Of course Miladin would be beside her to give her support: officially she was now in charge of the 1st *decetar* with Miladin as her deputy in Vukoye's *vod*, but she knew as well as Jovitch did that it was Miladin who provided the experience. She knew that there was always a slight fear in her *vod* that she might be taken prisoner; the Bulgars were not merciful to their prisoners; they were often tortured and usually killed. Miladin told her not to worry. As long as he was alive, she would not be taken prisoner. When she asked him what would happen if he was badly wounded first, he was rather evasive. She had an uncomfortable feeling that he would shoot her himself.

All through that long hot summer in Salonika, they trained: foot drill, musketry, route marches, mock attacks in extended order. One small privilege had been granted her: she was allowed to use a light carbine instead of the heavy rifle of French military pattern, the normal issue.

The rest of the world seemed very far away. They knew that on the Western Front the French had won a defensive battle at Verdun, but that the casualties had been very heavy; in Ireland there had been a rebellion; General Smuts had mounted a campaign in East Africa, and the Italians and Austrians were hammering away at each other in the mountains around Trentino. They had heard of a summer offensive by the resurgent Russian armies which had resulted in the capture of Stanislau, of a naval battle called Jutland and rumours of preparation for a huge offensive at a place called the Somme. But it was their activity in the regiment and when they were to go north to the front line which really concerned them, and nothing else. They were going to fight their way back through the mountains which rose along the northern border of Greece, back through Macedonia and Serbia to Belgrade and onwards into Bulgaria and Austria. If they succeeded, the German and Austrian Empires would face defeat.

It was a vastly different Serbian Army nowadays. Only 120,000 were left of the 650,000 who had been called to the colours at the outbreak of war. No longer was it an army of peasant reservists who sang as they marched and gathered in the harvest between battles. Those brown uniforms of homespun wool, braided with black lace, those sandals of camel-skin laced up the legs over stockings with embroidered tops, had rotted in the mud and slime of the retreat, the camel-skin shoes cracked, bloodied and abandoned somewhere in the mountains. Now their boots were British army issue, heavy and studded with nails; and they wore the horizon blue uniform of France, although Flora still kept the khaki jacket she had obtained in Corfu. Even the round sheepskin caps were now made of khaki cloth and on their packs they carried French army-pattern steel helmets.

Whether they accepted it or not, Serbia had ceased to exist. Its armies had been driven from its boundaries, its women and children and old folk, who had not fled the country or died in mountain passes, were overseas in refugee camps or living under the tyranny of the Bulgars.

Yet, as the months passed, they did not talk of the retreats but of the future. Flora listened to Jovitch, Vukoye and Doditch, in Jovitch's tent where they sat playing cards and drinking wine and endlessly talking. They talked of their families and friends and villages as if they were still unspoilt, as if the blossoms were still white on the fruit trees and the houses were as freshly painted as when they last saw them; as if their friends were waiting to greet them and toast their return; and of their mothers: *maika*, the mother, the most honoured woman in the family.

In the evenings, when they gathered round the camp fire with the rest of the company for a sing-song, Flora would watch them: Jovitch, with his air of authority, quick, incisive, suddenly looking at you with his deep blue eyes and friendly smile; Vukoye, gangling, whimsical, usually chewing a straw or a piece of grass, and Doditch, a most unlikely Slav, slim and fair, with his infectious laugh. They sang one new song which a soldier had written in Corfu: '*Tamo daleko, daleko cri mora, tamo je selo moya, tamo je lubar moya* . . . There far away, far away across the sea, that is my village; there is my heart.'

On Saturday night the four of them always went into town, Flora on the arm of her three gallant escorts. Off duty nobody cared about rank, and with her new sergeant's stars bright upon her shoulders, a woman sergeant was as good as a First Lieutenant any day, and twice as good as a Second Lieutenant, so she told Doditch and Vukoye as they swaggered along the waterfront.

For the soldier who came down from the front line, which stretched along the entire northern border of Greece, Salonika was more than a town; it was an oasis. In spite of the heat and the smells and the flies, you could swim in the warm sea and watch the garish sunset behind Mount Olympus. You could go to one of many noisy cabarets and beer halls and sing frenziedly in competition with Russians and Frenchmen and Italians and Aussies, newly arrived for the big offensive. After that you went up the line to the dust and heat and flies, the rocks and the mountains, and the inevitable whining of shells through the clear blue sky.

The night before they went up to the front Jovitch took her to dinner alone. First they went to Floca's. Anyone who was anybody went to Floca's, the officers with their girls, and the Greek merchants with their wives. Floca's was fashionable: the Café de Paris, the Piccadilly of Salonika.

Flora watched Janachko's face as he sat sipping his coffee. He was enjoying every minute of it. She hardly recognised him as the grim man she had first met outside Monastir when she presented the 4th Company with her little stock of jam and cigarettes and balaclavas. His chest wound had healed, and the bullet removed from his side; he was fit and sunburned. They were bound to win this war, he said. Serbia would be free and her hereditary enemies, Bulgaria, Austria and Turkey, defeated. Nothing could prevent a union of the Southern Slavs; a great new country would arise in the Balkans. They would drink to it. Sergeant Sandes smiled and did as she was told.

They dined afterwards in a small *taverna* at the back of the town. It was lit by tiny lamps and roofed with hanging vines. The tables were solid and the chairs rickety, most of the customers had big moustaches, large bellies, and loud voices. They ate *cous-cous* and *kebab* and drank pale yellow *retzina* out of a bottle without a label. And they talked about the war. It was practically the only experience they had in common. Then, because the war was far away and this was peace, with music and good food and wine, she deliberately changed the subject. Women, she murmured, what about the women in his life?

He paused, his glass halfway to his lips and looked astonished. 'Women,' repeated Flora. 'You've heard of them, and I want to know. You're not married, but you must have a sweetheart?'

He began to laugh. He threw back his head and roared, then he put down his glass and leaned on the table towards her.

'Sandes, you're very inquisitive,' he said. He shook his head, and there was no smile now. He had had no time for girls, only for war, he said. That's all, for the past three years. After the war, yes, but not now. Not now. His smile returned and his eyes crinkled. And what about her?

'No time at all,' grinned Flora, echoing him. 'No time until after the war.' They laughed together, and Janachko refilled her glass and they clinked the thick tumblers together and toasted, 'After the war!'

When they had paid the bill, they walked out into the narrow streets where the heat lay in wait for them, but it was cooler down by the sea, with the ships still and shadowy and the stars tumbling down the sky into the water. They talked and laughed as they went, and although it was a long way back to camp they did not notice the distance. They did not touch, they did not dream of kissing; after all, they were Lieutenant and Sergeant in the 'Iron Regiment'. And yet it was obvious they were more than just comrades-in-arms.

And now here they were aboard a train carrying the 2nd Regiment to the war. Soon it turned westwards and ran parallel with the mountains which rose sheer from the plain.

They left the train, marched northwards across broken country and camped that night in a broad, dried-out river bed. From her small tent Flora looked up the course of the river, littered with grey boulders and stones. In the river-bed were small grassy islands where tall stringy trees had taken root and dead leaves had piled themselves into heaps around their boles. As the wind blew, the leaves sighed, rustled, lifted, and then settled again. Through the thin branches she could see the outline of the hills held by the Bulgars, and behind them, misty-blue, the steep rise of the mountains. The sky was pale grey and here and there across it ran streamers of darker cloud. It would rain before morning, Flora decided.

She thought about the future. She knew that among these northern limits of Greece five divisions from Britain and three from France held a line roughly eighty miles in length, that already by the end of July the Serbs had taken over the left flank along the old Macedonian frontier. She knew her own Division, the Moravian Division, was going to take part in an all-out offensive, to drive the Bulgars from one mountain-top after another until they recaptured Monastir, and that the 2nd Regiment and its three thousand men, marching through the August heat, would fight courageously. What she did not know was that, by the time the November snows arrived, there would be less than five hundred of them left.

The next day they marched northwards along narrow dirt roads flanked by beeches, birches and larches, whose leaves flashed in the golden summer sunlight. The crops had been harvested: small streams gurgled down from the hills; fat white geese paddled in the gleaming shallows. Black and white magpies twisted against the multi-coloured hillsides, and beside the small, white-walled cottages lay heaps of orange water melons.

Before long they left the road and picked their way up into the hills. The rocks were grey and covered with lichen. The grass was short and springy, and the slopes grew steeper. Soon they could hear the guns like gentle thunder.

They slept for a few hours that night and moved forward again in the dawn. They halted at mid-day and waited for something to happen. Very soon it did. The Bulgar artillery started to shell them.

The noise of the shells increased as the enemy lobbed them across from the opposite valley. First came a faint whistle, suddenly growing in intensity, like the sound of an express train, then a fractional pause, and a tremendous bang as the high explosive shell bit into the rocky hillside. Huge pieces of rock and a hail of fragments were blown high into the air, occasionally rattling down on Flora's tin helmet.

After half an hour the barrage lifted and moved away. Her back against a rock, Flora half dozed. It was 5.30, almost dark. They had been standing by for hours, it seemed, waiting for the order to move forward. It was surely time now they got the order for a few hours' sleep.

She felt rather than heard the movement round her and, opening her eyes, saw Vukoye above her. 'We're moving up,' he said sharply.

'Now?'

'Now,' he answered. 'And we're taking only ammunition and knapsacks. Get ready!'

She sat bolt upright, aware of a tight feeling in her stomach. Miladin was kneeling beside her. 'You all right?' he asked, smiling.

She nodded. 'What are we doing?'

'Going into the line.'

Everywhere men were stirring: ten yards away two men were urinating against a rock. Closer still, another was scratching his armpit. None of this bothered her. Her time as a nurse had completed the gaps in her education.

Vukoye, his long legs moving at a pace which Flora found exhausting, led them at a smart trot down the hillside and through a stream at the bottom. The other side of the mountain was steep and so dark they could hardly see. Suddenly artillery opened up from somewhere, joined almost at once by sporadic rifle fire and grenades exploding.

They worked their way nearly to the crest of the hill, where a line of small holes had been dug, each just big enough to hold two people. Vukoye shouted an order, waved his arm, and the *vod* distributed themselves among the holes. Flora shared her dugout with Vukoye. It was half-full of mud and water.

'How long are we to stay here?'

'All night, as far as I know,' he said calmly.

'All night?' she echoed. 'But were do we sleep?'

'Here,' said Vukoye, patting the mud.

Flora kept her diary in her breast-pocket and, whenever she could, made a few notes, but carefully avoided all reference to regiments or numbers or locations, in case she was captured. On her first night in action she wrote: 'Slept a bit. About 1 a.m. order came to go forward again. Cold, pouring buckets, and blowing, awfully rough going on the hills. Got to the top of a stony rise where we lay on the stones on our tummies in pelting rain, with rifles and bombs ready, but nothing happened. Then forward again, blowing a gale and pitch dark, across some fields and up a stony hillside. Awfully cold at dawn and pretty wet, but managed to sleep for all that in my overcoat, no blanket; all that has to stay behind with the *Komorra* [mule transport]. Breakfast, cold stew brought up to us at 6 a.m. As soon as sun got up roasting hot, no shade. Stayed there on one spot until about 2 p.m.'

Shortly after dawn next morning their own artillery moved into position and hurled a barrage of shells at the enemy. The Bulgars replied, and Flora began to experience, for the first time, the unenviable fate of an infantryman sandwiched between artillery.

Lieutenant Vukoye outlined their role. At any moment a Very light would inform them that a rolling barrage had started some four hundred yards ahead of them. The 4th Company would advance in its wake.

He pointed out the line of advance which lay across a long open slope. They would dash across this first stretch in extended order, Vukoye explained, ten paces between each man, and take cover behind the next outcrop of rock.

His last words were almost drowned, as their own artillery opened up in the valley somewhere behind them, and they heard the regular swish and drone as the shells passed over them and burst four or five hundred yards ahead.

'Now!' yelled Vukoye, and Sergeant Miladin dashed forward

with Flora at his heels. His long legs at once took him ten yards ahead. She saw a great cloud of earth fly up somewhere over to her right and felt the blast in her face. Another blast and explosion on the left. Grimly she focussed on Miladin's broad back. If only they could reach the shelter of the rocks. Miladin dived to the ground. For a terrible second she thought he had been hit, but, throwing herself headlong beside him, she found he had only taken cover. She couldn't speak. Her chest heaved. She felt the short grass against her mouth, the earth and rock pressing reassuringly against her.

Suddenly she realized they were alone. She screwed her head right and left. No one. She peered behind her across the stretch of open ground. It was empty! The rest of the company was skulking in the shelter of the rocks way behind them. Miladin and she had raced forward by themselves; they could have run straight into a Bulgar position.

In a panic she began to get up, but felt his hand on her back. As he held her down, a volley of shells burst across the open grassland behind them. Miladin was quite calm. The Lieutenant had probably held the others back until the shelling died down a bit he explained.

They could still hear their own barrage thundering and rolling ahead of them. She looked around and just then saw a head rise cautiously from a near-by rock. She grabbed frenziedly for her rifle. It must be a Bulgar! Before she could swing it round a frightened voice called out in Serbian, 'Who are you?'

Miladin still had his hand on her back. Now he moved it to the barrel of her carbine and pushed it down. '4th Company, 1st Battalion, 2nd Regiment,' he answered cheerfully.

'All of it?' called the voice.

'Yes.' There was a short pause. 'Do you mind if I come over to die with the 4th Company?' asked the voice.

'Come,' said Miladin, and the man crawled across. He had lost his own Company. They were somewhere to the right or left, pinned down by the enemy shells. The thought of being killed all by himself depressed him, he explained. The Bulgar artillery soon stopped, and Vukoye and the rest of the *vod* came forward. Half an hour later their own artillery ceased firing and all was quiet.

Vukoye gave the signal and they crept onwards, expecting to hear the enemy machine-guns or at least rifle-fire at any moment.

But all was silent. It was almost eerie as they advanced cautiously up the rocky slopes with no sort of opposition. Either the Bulgars were lying concealed waiting for them to come within range or the Serbian guns had caught them by surprise.

The truth was soon revealed. The Bulgars had been caught unawares. Flora felt her stomach turn as they moved between the rocks. Bodies and bits of bodies were strewn everywhere, amidst the debris of guns and ammunition and equipment.

One hollow, where many smashed bodies lay, had been some sort of base camp. A salvo had scored a direct hit. Four Bulgars sat upright in the attitude in which death had caught them, staring at a pot of stew still bubbling on the camp-fire.

That night they made themselves comfortable in shelters recently occupied by the enemy, and Jovitch came across to see her. He could see she was upset and asked no questions. He had brought a bottle of brandy, and with Doditch and Vukoye they sat together in a dugout, taking turns to drink from it. Flora could not explain that she found the whole business utterly sickening. The horror of it had deeply affected her; she couldn't get it out of her mind.

For once they did not discuss the war; they talked about Salonika and the cabarets and the fun they had had there. Flora drank too much. She curled up in a corner and Jovitch tucked a blanket around her and said, 'Now go to sleep, you'll feel much better in the morning.' She remembered thinking, in her shocked, numbed mind, 'I'll never forget it, and I'll never get over it, and if I ever do, and can ever accept such things without sickness and horror, then I'm not a human being.'

II

During those weeks of mountain warfare which ended in disaster, Flora's life had a nightmarish quality. They fought their way through the mountains, counting their gains in yards and their casualties in hundreds, winkling the Bulgars out of their cracks and crannies in the rocks, repelling their counter-attacks, and Flora, enduring all the hardships as stoically as the next man, kept her sanity by simply looking no farther ahead than the next hour, the next meal and the next sleep.

It was no longer possible to glamorize war. Poor Lemuel Shuldham was no longer a poetic figure in her dreams; she could grieve for him as a comrade killed in battle, but now her grief was based on harsh reality.

On the Western Front they advanced three thousand yards in a week and lost a hundred thousand men, and a week later they were back where they had started; on the Eastern Front they advanced thirty miles in a week and lost an equivalent number of men, and a week later *they* were back where they started; in the mountains south of Monastir they advanced three hundred yards in a week, lost a thousand men, and clung on with fantastic determination to every rock and pebble. Never in the history of warfare had men been committed to such utter futility!

She wrote many letters from what soldiers in the last war called a 'slit trench', under the heading 'In a Funk Hole': 'If anyone at home begins asking me to describe the war I shall tell them to go into the back garden, dig a hole and sit there for anything from three days and nights to a month without a thing to do or read and they can judge for themselves—minus the chance of being killed of course . . . I found a poor devil of a badly wounded Bulgar near our dugouts in reserve. He had been lying there two days, left behind by the Bulgars before we came. No one was doing anything for him. You can hardly wonder at it, as the least the Bulgars do to our wounded and prisoners is to cut their throats. Our men simply leave them alone; you can hardly expect them to risk their lives carrying them a long way to the ambulance. I took to this chap because he had such spirit and wouldn't *kow-tow* to anyone. Though he was badly shot through both thighs, and couldn't move, and expecting every moment to be treated as they treat the Serbs, he lay there hurling abuse at everyone, and said if he had a rifle he would shoot us yet, and he was just a lad. I dressed his wounds and bandaged him up as well as I could, and gave him some water and a drink of brandy which he refused at first under the impression that it was poison. The poor chap was quite grateful, asked if I was a captain (I suppose because I had been cussing the men and making them get me bandages, etc.) and said I was a *silna brat* (fine brother). I got into a fearful row from our commandant of battalion who said he couldn't ever get his own men off to the ambulance, and that we had no business down there anyway, where they were shelling; but his bark is always much worse than his bite, and in the evening as soon as possible he had him carried down. . . . '

That evening, in the muddy squalor of their dugout, a hole between rocks with rocks piled either side and a roof made of sandbags packed with earth, Jovitch, who had been temporarily attached to battalion headquarters, came across to see how they were getting on. He had news for them. The 3rd Company had lost its second commander in two days; Jovitch was to take over until another could be appointed. Meanwhile Vukoye was to command the 4th, with Doditch as second-in-command.

Casualties had been heavy; though in their own group only Milosh had been injured, and his wound was a minor one. He had received a shell splinter in the calf and had been ordered back to the field hospital to have it dressed. He had gone off cursing, declaring that he would be back within hours.

She realised that the atmosphere at this time was rather like the height of the typhus epidemic in Valjevo. There were no heroics; you carried out your orders, derived what comfort you could from comradeship, and went on living. Whenever possible you joked and drank and gambled, and sang noisily. Long afterwards Flora wrote: 'Sometimes now when playing family bridge for threepence a hundred the memory of those wild nights comes over me, and I am lost in another world. So far away it all seems now, that I wonder whether it was really myself, or only something I dreamed. Instead of the powdered nose of my partner I seem to be looking at the grizzled head and unshaven chin of the Commandant, and the scented drawing-room suddenly fades away into the stone walls of a tiny hut lighted by a couple of candles stuck into bottles and thick with tobacco smoke, where five or six officers and I sit crowded on bunks or camp stools. For evening dress, mudstained, bloodstained khaki breeches and tunic, and for vanity bag a revolver. The camp table was covered by the thick brown folds of an army blanket, and before each was a pile of Serbian bank-notes and gold, and a tumblerful of red wine. Then came a batman with another relay of little cups of the thick, sweet Turkish coffee, which he brought about every hour. But here comes a trim maid with tea, and I return to the prosaic drawing-room with a start, and the realization that I am a "lady" now, not a "soldier and a man"; also that Serbian soil

МИНИСТАРСТВО ВОЈНО И МОРНАРИЦЕ
КРАЉЕВСТВА СРБА, ХРВАТА И СЛОВЕНАЦА

ОПШТЕ ВОЈНО ОДЕЉЕЊЕ
АЂУТАНТСКИ ОДСЕК
ФАО Бр. 141662

20. фебруара 1920. године
у Београду.

У В Е Р Е Њ Е

Министарство Војно и Морнарице овим уверава, да је МИС ФЛОРА САНДЕС, као резервни пешадиски наредник 1. чете 1. батаљона 2. пешадиског пука "Кнеза Михаила", указом Његовог Височанства Престолонаследника Александра од 18. јуна 1919. године ФАО Бр. 91813, на предлог Министра Војног и Морнарице, а по саслушању Министарског Савета, за нарочите заслуге и показану личну храброст у борбама на Солунском фронту, којом је приликом рањена и одликована златним војничким орденом Карађорђеве Звезде са мачевима, на основи члана 19. закона о устројству војске изузетно произведена у чин РЕЗЕРВНОГ ПЕШАДИСКОГ ПОТПОРУЧНИКА, са рангом од 20. априла 1919. године.

Уверење ово издаје се потпоручнику г. Сандесу на употребу.

Министар Војни и Морнарице
Ђенерал,
Јовановић

На служби, мајор,
[illegible]

МИНИСТАРСТВО ВОЈНО И МОРНАРИЦЕ
КРАЉЕВСТВА СРБА, ХРВАТА И СЛОВЕНАЦА

ОПШТЕ ВОЈНО ОДЕЉЕЊЕ
АЂУТАНТСКИ ОДСЕК
ФАО Бр. 141662

le 21 Fevrier 1920
BELGRADE.

C E R T I F I C A T.

Le Ministère de la Guerre et de la Marine certifie que Miss Flora SANDES ancien sergent major de reserve de la 1.er Cie du 1e Bon du 2e Régiment d'Infanterie "du Prince Michel" a été promue à titre éxceptionel au grade de St Lieutenant d'Infanterie de Reserve par Ukase de Son Altesse Royal le Prince Régent Alexandre FAO No. 91813 du 18 Juin 1919 pour prendre rang du 20 Avril 1919, et en vertu de l'article 19. de la Loi sur l'organisation de l'Armée.

Cette Nomination a été faite après déliberation du Conseil des Ministres, sur proposition du Ministre de la Guerre et de la Marine, en consequence des services particulièrs rendus par Miss Flora SANDES à l'Armée, ainsi que pour sa bravour dans les combats au front de Salonique, où elle a été glorieusement blessée et a recu les insignes de l'Etoile d'or de Karageorge avec glaives pour soldats.

Général Ministre de la Guerre
et de la Marine
Yovanovitch

Commandant
[illegible]

МИНИСТАРСТВО ВОЈНО И МОРНАРИЦЕ — КРАЉЕВСТВА СРБА ХРВАТА И СЛОВЕНАЦА

Official citation confirming Flora Sandes as the first woman ever to be commissioned in the Serbian Army

An end-of-the-war celebration. Sergeant-Major Sandes toasts a comrade on his wedding day

The war is over. Flora Sandes relaxing on the banks of the Vardar

is resting lightly on the graves of many of those happy comrades I have been seeing in my dreams.'

Her closest companion was Lieutenant Jovitch, with whom she shared a deep and lasting relationship. She sometimes wondered if love could ever blossom in the blood and exhaustion of battle, but in her short, laconic diary written in the intervals of battle, she refers practically every day to some aspect of how they lived . . . 'Had supper at ambulance, got back at nine p.m. and found that Janachko had gone to Battalion Staff to replace Voyau wounded . . . Janachko came and woke me up at six a.m. He had been playing cards and wanted a drink . . . Lovely moonlight night, J. had supper with me and we sat around it afterwards . . . Sat about all morning and scrapped with J. . . . Had supper with Battalion Staff and slept with them on some straw near well, and shared Janachko's blanket . . . Played cards in afternoon with Battalion Staff, lost 100 drachmas, had supper with them and played all night until 8 a.m., great night, lost fifty drachmas. Janachko came in afterwards and jawed me like the devil for gambling . . . Found J. asleep on my bed when I came to turn in . . . Rode over to Divisional Staff to ask for leave for Janachko and me to go to Salonika.'

There was frustration in this growing awareness of love between them. A sergeant and Lieutenant could not fall in love with each other in the middle of a war. Not officially, anyway. But in those rocky holes in the mountainside, sometimes as black as pitch, sometimes with the moonlight clear and hard as day, to the inevitable rumble of artillery and the sighing and bursting of star shells, they needed to lie close to each other for human warmth, for reassurance that outside the barren world of hate and destruction, within themselves, lay the seeds of a new life.

The future held one hope for them. When the winter snows finally set in and both armies were bogged down, leave would be granted. Flora applied to Divisional Headquarters for permission for them to go on leave together to Salonika. Salonika meant music and peace and contentment.

On September 13 she wrote: 'Awful pull at the double over open rocky ground. We had to cross one short open place under fire, and to lie on our tummies and scrabble a few stones together for our heads, the others ran across, but I simply couldn't run so walked and got there last. Vukoye's orderly got badly hit, internal haemorrhage, died next day in Field Ambulance. We only lay there about half an hour, then back again. Went to a steep hill and lay on the stones there with bullets whizzing around. I crawled to a place where I stood up for a minute and took two photos. Sat there all morning, broiling hot. Bulgars shelling opposite hillside facing us which we had come over. Then went forward and chased them all day over the most awful hills and stones, I don't know how many miles. We got to a hill with trees where we could see them about 1,000 to 1,500 yards and had a great shooting match at long range. I used up all my ammunition. Saw Vukoye bring one down with my carbine at 1,000 yards. Passed a village where the 22nd Regiment took nineteen heavy guns and prisoners. The Bulgars had evacuated; saw one wounded sitting in a trench. I don't know what became of him. We got right ahead and 1st *Vod* ahead of everybody. Later on Michaelo in charge of ordnance and Janachko came up. Not quite sure where Bulgars were, and they said we should all be taken prisoner. Broiling hot, nothing to eat until suppertime. I borrowed some ammunition. As soon as it got dark we moved to another spot where we dug ourselves in and spent the night. Rained. I was so tired I could hardly crawl and lay down on the stones and slept soundly until 1 a.m. when I moved into dugout with Janachko. Moonlight.'

The next day was almost the same: 'Soon after dawn moved on to another hillside. I stopped by a well and got a wash and was following up 1st *Vod*, fell in with Comm. Battalion and Janachko and we got into a violent bombardment. Sat under a mound until it got too hot for us, shells bursting all round, so we made series of short moves to rocky rise. After lunch 4th. Co. went forward and 1st *Vod* took up position in a field where we lay and scorched our skin off on the stones, and could not move again until dusk. The Bulgars about 1,500/2,000 yards away, but peppered us whenever we lifted our noses. Wrote a letter as it was too long a range for my carbine. At dusk we moved a little way to village Krushegrad where we spent the night. Washed and vaselined my feet as I was very footsore. Moonlight night and fine, but very cold.'

Miladin was worried about Lieutenant Jovitch. He did not mind so much loaning him to Battalion H.Q. Major Pesitch would look after him, as he looked after every other man under his command, but the 3rd Company had no right to the 4th's commanding officer. They had lost two already, which surely proved that they did not know how to 'look after' their officers. The 3rd Company was unlucky, Miladin declared. They would not 'take care' of Jovitch. Something must be done about it.

This idea of taking care of one's officer went right through the Serbian Army. Two weeks before, Major Pesitch had told Flora with some amusement how his own orderly had 'looked after' him; he had stolen his epaulettes. The orderly had rightly decided that snipers were always on the look-out for the distinguishing marks of an officer and that the Major should run no risk. Consequently he removed his epaulettes. When Pesitch woke to find them missing, he was furious. At once he accused his orderly who admitted his theft, but made it plain that no military punishment would prevent him doing the same thing again while they were in action. Major Pesitch fumed and promised a shooting squad, but finally did nothing. Fortunately, the very next day, an order came from Divisional Headquarters absolutely prohibiting the wearing of epaulettes by all officers on active service.

Sunday, October 15, was a discouraging day. It was cold, they had not advanced as far as they had expected, and the company had lost quite a few men from artillery fire. At dusk they suddenly made a move up the hill to their right. 'Vukoye made one of his sudden bolts and we all pelted after him,' reported Flora. 'We went through a hailstorm of bullets or at least it seemed like that to me.'

The sudden rush ended some distance up the mountainside behind a rock. Dragutin proved his worth as an orderly by digging a hole in which she immediately went to sleep, while Vukoye lay down behind the rock.

She was roused in the middle of the night by Vukoye whispering into her ear. They doubled forward and at the same time the Bulgars, who seemed to sense what was up, opened fire. Bullets seemed to be coming from all directions. Vukoye wriggled away into the darkness, and Flora looked across at Miladin who said they would stay where they were. The Lieutenant would be back when he had made up his mind what they were going to do.

Sure enough, a red Very light suddenly shot into the air thirty yards in front of them and to their right, and they knew Vukoye had fired the signal. Suddenly she heard Dragutin's voice calling her urgently. She must come across at once, for the Lieutenant was wounded. She slung her carbine across her shoulders and doubled off in the direction which Dragutin had indicated. As she came closer, she heard Vukoye cursing and muttering to himself. He was crouching behind a rock. He had foolishly raised his right arm to fire the Very pistol and a bullet had passed clean through it.

She cut open his sleeve. It was too dark to examine the wound properly as she applied the field dressing, but the bone did not seem to be broken. She ordered him back to the ambulance tent. but he refused. Flora was secretly relieved, knowing how depressing an effect the absence of a commanding officer could have on a company's morale.

Dawn was beginning to break through a pale grey mist, when Doditch crawled across from his *vod*. Vukoye was now looking very white indeed, and Flora knew he would have to go back for medical attention sooner or later. He tried to force his long, melancholy face into a grin, but wasn't very successful. He had lost a lot of blood.

Doditch, his boyish features worried beneath his steel helmet, suggested that they pull back their *vod* on a line with his own; they were too far advanced here and had both flanks exposed. Vukoye agreed reluctantly; a few yards of mountainside was territory not easily regained. They all edged their way down cautiously.

Vukoye went back to the rear, and Sergeant-Major Rangel, one of the oldest and best of the senior N.C.O.s, came across to take over the 1st *Vod*. News then reached them that the 3rd Company would pass through them in the night and take over the forward positions. Flora hoped she would have a chance of a word with Jovitch. Rangel decided that as the Bulgars had not apparently moved down, the six of them, Flora, Miladin, Mirko, Dratza, Dragutin and himself, would go forward to their more exposed position of the previous night to try and give the enemy the impression that they were there in force. As soon as darkness fell they set off, crawling stealthily forward. There were several extra rifles lying in the ravine, left there by the wounded, and they each took one with them.

Before dawn, in the early hours of the morning, when they thought they heard the sound of the Bulgars preparing an attack, they each poked out two rifles and blazed away simultaneously. The ruse apparently intimidated the enemy, because they heard no more. As the dawn began to break, the 3rd Company moved up to them and then past, wriggling cautiously through the rocks and across the open spaces.

She heard a 'pssst' behind her, a favourite signal of Janachko's, and knew it was him. He crawled up beside her and sprawled out, grinning and quite happy. Yes, he'd seen Vukoye as he went down; he would be back in action within a few days. And as soon as this particular mountain had been captured, he, Jovitch, was coming back to take command of his 4th company again; old Pesitch had assured him of that. He smiled as he spoke, put his hand on her forearm and squeezed it. He was still bronzed from the Salonika sun, and in the pale light his eyes were very blue, and his teeth white against his skin.

Flora repeated what Miladin had said about the 3rd not looking after its officers properly. He must be very careful. Janachko's eyebrows shot up in mock surprise. He, careful? Surely she knew he was the very epitome of caution. Besides, within an hour their barrage would be opening up, blasting the Bulgar positions and making them untenable. All they would have to do was take a nice quiet stroll up the mountainside collecting all the loot including the German binoculars and the Mauser revolvers. Was there anything she particularly wanted? He squeezed her arm again, gave her a last smile and was gone.

Two hours later it happened. It was grey and cold: Rangel lay on her right side, Ylenko on her left, with the others scattered nearby. She heard the 'Hurrish', and knew it was not the sound of the 3rd Company charging but the enemy counter-attacking! She peered over her rock. There was quite a sizeable open space, perhaps fifty yards of tufted grass and shale, between her and the next rocky outcrop. It was deserted, but suddenly she saw three men of the 3rd Company come racing back across it. Something had gone wrong.

The wild '*Houra-houra*' of the Bulgars was closer now. The rest of the 3rd Company broke from their fox-holes above and ran; they pounded towards her and past her, their faces contorted with fear, intent only on escape.

Flora's courage drained from her. She twisted her head to look across at Sergeant-Major Rangel. She saw him half rise, his mouth opened to shout a rallying-call, and then he pitched forward and on to his face in the dirt. She knew that he was dead. To her left Ylenko was dead, too; she saw the small round hole in his forehead as he mouthed something and jerked forward on to the ground.

The 3rd were all round her now, crashing past her down the mountainside. As she wrote later: 'Once a Company has lost its head not even an angel with a flaming sword could stop them.' The 4th Company, stampeded by the flight of the 3rd, turned and fled with them.

Gripped by panic, she began to run, too. She collided with Dragutin who was just behind her. 'Run, run!' he called, his dark eyes bulging with fear. Then she heard the voice of the Captain of the Battalion H.Q. shouting from somewhere over to the right at the top of his voice: '4th Company forward! 4th Company forward!' It was a direct order, and scared though she was, Flora knew she had to obey. She turned on her heel, her heart pounding, but knowing somehow she must get up to where the Captain was calling. He was thirty yards farther up the hill, sheltering behind a rock, his runner beside him, and scribbling an order in his despatch book. When she was still twenty yards away, he thrust the message into the runner's hand.

Just then Flora became aware that Dragutin was still at her heels, protesting. Was she mad? Did she want them both to get killed?

She reached the rock where the Captain stood. He looked at her in surprise. She was too breathless and too scared to say a word. The charging Bulgars were now so close she could almost hear the sound of their feet. 'Come on,' snapped the Captain, 'run for it.'

He shot past her down the slope with Dragutin after him. Flora was now last in the procession. She knew that their objective was the ravine where they had found shelter earlier, but it seemed miles away. Somehow she gained a little on the Captain and was now less than ten yards behind him. Bullets whistled around her. What she did not hear was the sound of three bullets fired at her by the best marksman in the 4th Company, Sergeant-Major Milosh.

He had left the ambulance tent that morning and had come forward to rejoin his Company. Losing his way in the unfamiliar terrain, he had reached a point above the ravine just in time to see the 3rd run for their lives and stampede his own Company as well. He had immediately flung himself down beside the two Serbian soldiers manning the outpost and begun to fire, when he saw a Serbian officer running full tilt down the hillside chased by a mad Bulgar in khaki; only a madman would have exposed himself so recklessly to the Serbian fire. He aligned the khaki figure in his sights and squeezed the trigger. The khaki figure did not fall or stop and he thought something must be wrong with his sights: he grabbed the rifle of the soldier next to him. He fired twice more, but missed both times. By this time the khaki figure had disappeared into the ravine behind the officer, and Milosh, annoyed at his poor markmanship, picked up his own rifle, identified a small white rock on the ground at the exact point where the Bulgar had been when he fired the first shot. He aimed and fired. The white rock kicked up into the air, shattered by the bullet.

He had a sudden, chilling thought. The elusive Bulgar had shown no nervousness when diving into the ravine held by the Serbs . . . Sergeant Sandes had never given up that khaki uniform she got for the regiment in Corfu. He gave the soldier back his rifle, and, when asked if he felt all right, growled something unintelligible. It was many days before he summoned up enough courage to tell Flora what he had done, but by then it did not matter to her.

In the ravine she immediately sought out and confronted Miladin. Why had they run? Why had *he* run? He looked at her silently, stroked his moustache and invited her to share his hole behind a large stone. Flora wedged herself in beside him while he tried to explain the psychology of panic. There was no point in feeling ashamed, he said. In certain circumstances even the bravest men in the world would run. She had not run only because she had not had enough experience. Sometimes you ran or you died. Slowly she accepted his reasoning.

Within half an hour it began to rain heavily, and the hole which Miladin had so laboriously scraped out now looked like a drain. Bullets were still ricocheting, but the Bulgars seemed content merely to exchange fire. It was cold and wet and miserable. To keep up her spirits, she began to recite 'The Charge of the Light Brigade'. Miladin listened with polite interest; he did not understand a single word, but knew that men used prayers in times of stress, and that this might be a good one.

It was now growing dark. The cold became fiercer and so did their hunger. Hopefully they both turned out the pockets of their overcoats, and to their surprise and joy found in one corner of Flora's pocket a squashed packet containing five cigarettes, and in the bottom of Miladin's knapsack a large mouldy crust. They crouched in the bottom of the wet hole, struck a match and drew their cigarettes into life. Miladin divided the bread in half and they began to chew happily.

Jovan, a tall, thin, young replacement, smelling the cigarette smoke, put his head up over a rock four yards away to see what was happening. There was a sudden clang as a bullet passed clean through his steel helmet and the top of his head. He made no protest but rolled over towards them. He knew, as they all did, of Flora's skill as a nurse.

Blood was gushing through the hole in the helmet and for a second Flora thought he was done for, but when Miladin eased off his helmet and she clamped her hand tightly against the wound, he was still conscious. She remembered her old St John's Ambulance lectures: 'Lay the wounded man down in a comfortable position and apply pressure to the spot'. Jovan was half-in and half-out of the watery hole, almost crushing her. She scrambled into a kneeling position and told Miladin to find a field dressing.

She fastened it around Jovan's head. He was conscious, and apparently not in great pain; but she did not like the look of his wound. He would roll away down the hill, he said; the ambulance men could pick him up at the bottom. He thanked them solemnly for their help. Flora lit up one of the damp cigarettes and pushed it between his lips before he went sliding and rolling down the steep slope. She wiped the blood off her hands on a tuft of wet grass and took a long pull on her cigarette.

It rained all that night and well into the next day. Dragutin was wounded, though not seriously, and grumbling furiously at his misfortune left for the base hospital. She spent twenty-four hours in a small hole not five yards from a dead Bulgar, and at last during the night they went down the mountainside and into reserve. Dawn was breaking, its grey light suddenly picking out the colours in the rocks, the green grass in sheltered overhangs, and the faces of her comrades, thin and exhausted.

They were still high up, working down a steep escarpment into a wide valley. At a bend in the track Major Pesitch was waiting for her. He stood aside to allow the first few men to shuffle past, then took her arm and led her to a point where the rocks fell sheer to the valley below.

She knew it was most unusual for him to draw her aside, and she felt sure he had bad news for her. He told her that the rest camp where they were going stood on the top of a high mountain about ten miles behind the line. It was a beautiful spot covered with huge fir trees and they would be at peace for a week or ten days. But she knew he hadn't taken her aside to tell her this, and she dreaded his next words. Quietly and briefly he told her that Janachko had been killed. Lieutenant Janachko Jovitch, commander of the 4th Company, who had been advanced from private to commissioned rank within two years, who had fought a hundred gallant battles against his country's enemies, was dead.

She sat there, looking blindly into the valley while two eagles drifted past, high against the blue emptiness.

Janachko had been with the 3rd the day they broke under the counter-attack, he told her. He had been right up in the advance position. Of course he had not run when the 3rd broke. He had that deep inner certainty that God would protect him. He had stood up and waved them forward and led them out to meet the enemy. The bullet had killed him instantly.

They had recovered his body when the Bulgars retired next day. Like Lemuel, thought Flora. Like Lemuel, 'far in advance within the sight of French lines his body was found next morning and buried on the spot'.

No, they had not buried him on the spot, Pesitch told her. They had brought his body back and buried it down below in the valley near the village church of Dobro Veni.

Two days later she went down with him. Dobro Veni, which means 'Sweet Flower', had miraculously escaped the shelling. When the priest heard why they had come he gave Flora two white candles to place on the grave. It stood alone on the hillside, a rough oblong of piled stones. Flora wedged the candles in between the rocks and lit them. The little flames wavered, then burned steadily.

Did she love him? If it was love to feel safe and secure when the other was near; if it was love to know by a swiftly exchanged look what the other was thinking; if it was love to huddle together in the night, sharing a blanket and the warmth of another's body, then theirs was a love of an uncommon kind. Platonic? Only in the outward sense of the word because, from the very first, their relationship had never been on a very pure or spiritual plane. To each other they had brought not only passion and conflict, but comfort and consolation.

Now it was all over: the year, born in the bleak winter of the Albanian retreat, and continuing through the green months of the Corfu spring and the hot and golden Salonikan summer, was now ended here where it began, in the middle of a battle.

She wished she could gather even a small posy of flowers to lay on the flinty stones that covered his body, but the mountains of Macedonia in that valley were too hard and too sterile, it seemed, to produce even a single blossom.

Chapter Eight

I

THE STRIP of wet sacking which masked the doorway of their dugout was pulled aside and Vukoye's bony frame edged its way through. He brushed the snow from the sleeves of his overcoat and banged his cap on his knee, scattering flakes over Flora and Doditch.

'Mind the chessmen,' she protested, protecting the pocket board. 'Even if the war lasts another hundred years, Doditch is going to learn how to play.'

Doditch's brow was furrowed with concentration. 'War is simpler,' he said.

Flora looked at Vukoye, giving him time to settle before she asked him the question which concerned them all. He caught her glance and nodded. 'Tomorrow,' he said, 'tomorrow night as soon as it's dark.'

Recovered from his arm wound, he had returned to take over the 4th. Jovitch's death had shocked him as deeply as the rest of the company. For one entire day they had all refused to eat. It was the only gesture they could make to show their grief and respect. The numbness which Flora felt had still not worn off. She tried to conceal it beneath a veneer of lightheartedness; she could play chess with Doditch and joke about how badly he played; she could tell herself that time cured all the ills; but deep down she did not think she would ever find cómfort.

'Cold stew again,' said Vukoye disgustedly, examining the bottom of the billy-can, 'even the Bulgars must do better than this.'

'Is it dark enough yet?' asked Flora. Vukoye drew back the sacking. 'Dark and no stars,' he said, twisting his knees round so that she could get past. She heard him scraping the pot with his bent spoon as she let fall the sacking behind her. She remembered Vukoye's old dictum; daylight destroys you, darkness hides. It was true. The sun, if it appeared at all, disappeared about five o'clock in the afternoon, and it was dark half an hour later. Then they could come out and a meal of some sort would arrive from base.

It was an oddly circumscribed world. They knew which regiment held the left flank and which regiment defended the right; and they knew that the Bulgars occupied the mountain above them which had been named Hill 1212.

Only Hill 1212 stood between them and the capture of Monastir which it dominated. From some points on the ridge they could see the town far away up the valley, the winter sun reflected from its minarets, a few stray wisps of smoke floating upwards.

On these rocky slopes Jovitch had died and 2,500 men of the Second Regiment had become casualties. Of the 3,000 veterans who had marched to the railhead in Salonika, only 500 men and Flora Sandes were left for the final assault. Hill 1212 had become the graveyard of the Second Regiment.

Across the valley one enormous peak, shaped vaguely like the Matterhorn, reared high into the air, its high, flat faces of sheer, grey rock powdered with freshly fallen snow. When dawn came, they would lift their sacking curtain and watch it glowing in the early-morning sun.

It was a lovely sight and sometimes they would pretend they were sitting in a sunny hollow far down below, the thick trees protecting them from the wind, the river running deep and green near their feet; by contrast their own world, high up on this exposed ridge, was cold and comfortless.

It was Flora's own choice that she was there at all. The Colonel, foreseeing the agony ahead, had done his best to leave her behind during their period in reserve on top of the fir-covered mountain. Ten days in reserve they were told, and Flora, still grieving at Janachko's death, knew she could not stand so long a period of inactivity. She thought of Ostrova. Why couldn't she go there? It wasn't many miles to the rear. Ostrova at any time was idyllic: a green hollow in the hill near the lake; a clump of ancient elm trees and a vast sheet of water in the background. The Scottish Women's Hospital was setting up a huge casualty clearing-station, and women from all over the world were helping to run it: British, American, Canadian, Australian. It would be pleasant to talk to women again.

She appealed to Doditch, who made no objection so long as Colonel Militch was informed. The Colonel's tent was half a mile away. He gave her coffee and courteously offered her a seat. Go to Ostrova for a few days? An excellent idea. She could borrow a horse and set off at that very moment without bothering to return to her *vod*.

Flora thanked him, finished her coffee, and walked out into the winter sunshine. She looked across at the horse-lines and hesitated; perhaps, after all, she should go back and tell Doditch that the Colonel had granted her request. The uphill scramble took her longer than she expected and, when she reached her *vod*, she saw at once that they were packing up, getting ready to move.

'Ten days' rest,' said Miladin mournfully. 'We're setting off for the front at 3 a.m.' He stared at her, 'I thought you had gone to Ostrova.'

'That was the plan,' said Flora, 'but it's too late now.'

Even then she did not realise the extent of the Colonel's duplicity. They started down the mountainside in the dark, and as usual it began to rain. At the bottom they found themselves in thick undergrowth. Plodding through this tangled morass in pitch darkness without the least idea where they were going, Flora decided she had been mad not to accept the Colonel's offer.

At mid-day they halted to eat their bread ration. While they were finishing, the Colonel and his staff rode up. Flora saw him glance in her direction and rein to a halt. Lieutenant Michaelo came over and said that the Colonel would like a word with her.

Flora walked across. She saluted and the Colonel studied her with interest.

'Sandes, I thought I'd got you off to Ostrova,' he said. 'What are you doing here?'

Flora told him what had happened. When she got back, she had found the 4th preparing to move up to the front.

The Colonel looked at her thoughtfully. That information was quite incorrect, he told her. They were only going to hold some lines of communication near another reserve. She would have time to take several days' leave; if she cared to choose any horse a member of his staff was riding, she could set off at once.

Flora saluted and thanked him. She felt relieved; she eyed the horses and was just deciding that she had better borrow one belonging to a junior officer, when the Colonel made his big mistake.

'I'm sorry,' he said to his staff, 'but one of you gentlemen will have to walk. However, I think it's worth it.'

He spoke to them in Serbian. From his very first meeting with Flora, he had always talked to her in German; and, although she had been with the regiment for more than a year, he was still under the impression that she spoke little or no Serbian. He went on, 'We're going right into the thick of it, and I'd rather she wasn't killed.'

Flora's mouth tightened. Carefully choosing her words, so as to reveal her excellent knowledge of his language, she informed him that she was most grateful for his consideration, but at a time like this she preferred to stay with her own company.

Colonel Militch smiled and accepted the rebuff graciously. 'Sergeant Sandes,' he said mildly, 'return to your company.' He paused, gravely returning her salute. 'And good luck!' he added quietly.

That evening they moved up on to the flanks of Hill 1212, and the next seven days were amongst the most miserable she ever remembered.

Even when Vukoye brought the order that they were to move up into the line the following night, they knew it meant no relief. Flora hated night marches. In the darkness you could never see where you were going; or where your objective was or how much ground you had covered.

It had rained and snowed almost constantly for the past two days and as they climbed higher and higher in the darkness the ground under their feet became a lane of deep mud. They stopped once for a breather and she heard the man behind her coughing and gasping. He slumped back against a rock.

It was a man in her platoon called Shuster—the shoemaker. She knew he had T.B., so she tried to think of something to say to help him.

He was determined, he said, speaking in gasps, to keep up with her; as long as she went on, he would too.

It was still dark when they reached their destination, and Flora slumped wearily to the ground, drew her overcoat tight, and like the rest of the sprawling bodies around her fell into a deep, exhausted sleep.

Dawn was only a pale lightening of the sky behind the mountains when she was woken by Vukoye. In front of them, running right across the mountain slope like a natural barricade, she could see a high spine of rocks. 3rd Company were higher up on the other side of it, and higher still, hard against the Bulgar positions, were the companies of the 1st Regiment whom they were going to relieve. 4th Company's job was to act as battalion reserve, he told her, and Major Pesitch's Battalion H.Q. lay in a cluster of rocks not fifty yards away.

The snow was thick. The enemy remained absolutely silent. After Vukoye's whispered comments there seemed nothing else to do but try and get some more sleep, so Flora carefully rearranged her overcoat collar, pulled her cap down over her ears, wrapped herself tightly in her mackintosh sheet and snuggled down.

She was dreaming that wild bearded men were racing towards her when she awoke to realise that the increasing crackle of gunfire and the distant voices shrieking *'Houra! Houra!'* were no dream at all. The Bulgars were charging down upon them.

She threw aside her mackintosh and grabbed for her carbine. She felt sick in the pit of her stomach, so frightened that had it not been for the others all around her she would certainly have run for her life. A messenger came racing across from Major Pesitch; he called something to Vukoye which she did not hear. All around they were grabbing knapsacks and rifles. Against the grey dawn sky she could see their faces, so recently torn from sleep: unshaven chins, hollow cheeks, eyes bright with fear and excitement. In the icy air their breaths spurted like steam from their mouths. Lieutenant Vukoye shouted, 'Fix bayonets!'

In the half-light the steel gleamed dully as bayonets clattered out of scabbards. The metal hilt was cold and heavy to her numb fingers as she slotted the blade home.

'Drugi Vod napred!' snapped Vukoye. 'Second *Vod* forward!'

Flora had never known such fear before. This was the moment she dreaded: an impending clash with the enemy in hand-to-hand fighting. Surely the First Regiment would repulse their charge; perhaps this was one of those false alarms, the enemy attack would dwindle away as quickly as it started.

They started forward through a narrow gap in the wall of rock. The snow-drifts were deep and their feet sank in halfway up their calves. Two yards past the gap a man had fallen, his blood reddening the snow around his head. They were now under severe fire too. Flora was comforted to see the tall figure of Miladin just ahead of her, and the shorter bulk of Milosh by her side.

Major Pesitch stood on a rock as they filed through; it was a conspicuous position, but he seemed unaware of the flying bullets. 'Hurry, Vukoye, hurry!' he shouted. 'Help the 3rd, help the 3rd!'

The *vod* broke into a run. Once clear of the barrier of rocks they could see up the mountain slope, which ran upwards at a steep angle and was dotted with rocks of varying sizes. Behind each of them single soldiers or groups were crouching and firing into the drifting curtain of mist across the slope two hundred yards further up. It had acted as a smoke screen for the Bulgars' advance, who now advanced under its cover while their comrades poured a concerted stream of rifle and machine-gun bullets down at the Serbians.

In their first charge the Bulgars had broken through the First Regiment, and it was the remnants of this regiment, together with the 3rd Company, who now lay scattered, dead, dying or utterly demoralised on the slope. Major Pesitch knew that the only way to prevent a catastrophe was to counter-attack hard and fast.

Lieutenant Vukoye turned aside to threaten with his revolver a group of 3rd Company soldiers crouching behind a rock. He yelled an order for Miladin and Milosh to harry other groups, every man must attack. He ran across the slope yelling, 'Forward! Forward!'

Twenty yards in front Doditch was scrambling upwards at the head of a small group. He took cover by flopping down in the snow, and Flora and her men followed suit.

She heard wild blasts on a bugle from somewhere behind. The regimental bugler had panicked and Major Pesitch had grabbed his instrument. High on a rock, an easy target for any sniper, he was blowing as if his lungs would burst; the meaning was plain: 'Forward!'

Doditch obeyed. Even the frozen snow clutched in Flora's fingers seemed infinitely preferable to the fantastic hazard of leaping to her feet and racing towards that grey and lethal curtain of mist through which the bullets were whining and ricocheting. But she had to charge! She knew the order of advancing. A thirty-yard dash and you threw yourself on your face again. All she had to cover was thirty yards! Thirty little yards! She drew in her breath and scrambled up, conscious that the rest of her platoon were up with her. Together they raced after Doditch.

Her feet thudded over the frozen snow. She could see that bullets were kicking up little gouts of snow everywhere. Someone grunted and toppled over; she heard the noise of men screaming with the frenzy of the charge, yelling in madness and excitement and fear.

Five yards ahead she saw the Lieutenant throw himself on his face again. Three yards to her right Mirko did the same in a sprawling dive which tobogganned him forward.

They were now in the mist which seemed to be spreading and curling down towards them. As her knees buckled to slide to the ground, her eyes dilated with fear. Out of the mist, ten paces ahead, figures appeared; dark khaki-clad figures.

She saw their arms swing back and then up as they hurled their grenades. She saw the black blobs of metal fly through the air. She heard the thunder of the explosions, saw the snow lit with bright yellow flashes, and realized that they were so close to the Bulgars that the grenades had sailed over their heads; ten yards back and they would have been massacred. Too late she realized that ten yards was not enough.

With blinding suddenness the world disintegrated. An enormous sideways kick smashed her to the ground. She couldn't see; a black screen cut off the light. She couldn't move. She felt agonising pain, and even worse than the pain, an acute awareness that her *vod* was in full flight, that she was being left behind to die in the snow. All of them, including Lieutenant Doditch, were pounding away in mad terror-stricken flight.

Something brushed across her face and instinctively she reached up with her left hand. She wondered why her right hand and arm did not obey the frantic signal from her brain. Then her body jerked and she felt herself being towed backwards through the snow. The pain inside her was almost unbearable but instinct told her to hang on. Something gave and she fell back . . .

Lieutenant Doditch saw the enemy loom out of the mist, and flung himself to the ground as the grenades exploded. He heard the screams of the wounded, but at that moment did not realize he had been hit in three places himself, and that every man in the platoon had been wounded: one had a broken arm, another had his face split from forehead to chin.

The enemy hurled their bombs and dived for cover. He began to panic. On this snowy slope, in such an exposed position, with the Bulgar behind the rocks, they were dead ducks. The next swirl of mist would reveal them to the enemy, who would then pick them off at leisure. At any second he expected a bullet to smash into his body.

He bawled an order, scrambled up and turned to run. A body lay in his path and, without thinking, he jumped over it and raced onwards. He was scared to death. He hardly felt the heavy weight suddenly attach itself to his overcoat. He ran madly for the shelter of the rocks, feeling the tug as the buttons were ripped from his overcoat, but not knowing or caring what was happening. Suddenly the weight had gone and he almost flew the last ten yards into the shelter of the rocks.

A second later Milosh and Mirko flopped down beside him.

'Sandes,' panted Milosh, 'Sandes. She's out there. She's dead!'

Doditch peered over his rock: a bundle he recognised as Sergeant Sandes was sprawled in the snow fifteen yards up the slope. Fifty yards further on lay the rocks behind which the Bulgars were sheltering and exchanging fire. At last he understood. The weight he felt, his buttons ripping, must have been Sandes. She had grabbed the tail of his coat as he stepped over her, and he had towed her through the snow. Dead or alive, she had to be brought in, and he was the one who had to do it.

'Give me covering fire,' he snapped harshly to Milosh.

Flora slowly regained consciousness. Something lay under her cheek, smooth and cold. She heard shouting, rifles firing, and made a huge effort to open her eyes. There was whiteness under her face and she knew it was snow: glistening white snow, but lower down it was red. Slowly she realised that her blood was spreading in a widening stain beneath her.

She felt a quick surge of panic. She was wounded and they had left her to die. She couldn't move and she would just lie there and die.

A voice close to her whispered urgently, 'Stretch out your hand! For God's sake, stretch out your hand!'

She wondered vaguely why someone wanted her to stretch out her hand. She tried to obey but nothing would move, neither her hand, arm nor leg: nothing. Then she saw that it was Doditch. Odd that Doditch should be asking her to stretch out her hand;

what a silly thing for him to ask. Her head felt fuzzy; it was hard to breathe. All she wanted to do was just lie there quietly.

Now he was fumbling around her body. He'd caught hold of her right wrist. He wriggled away from her, pulling at her wrist. He tugged. And then the pain began. Mother of God, the pain! Her right arm was smashed and he was using it to tow her through the snow. She moaned and tried to mouth something coherent. But he took no notice and went on dragging her out of her bloody patch of snow. Inch by inch, yard by yard, panting and gasping, he dragged her backwards into the shelter of the rock.

Milosh slid forward to help him over the last two yards. Behind the rocks he had spread out his mackintosh sheet, and together they levered her body on to it. Peering over the rocks, Mirko fired two quick rounds. The Bulgars were moving down towards them, he reported. As he spoke, a grenade sailed through the air and exploded just short of the rock. Doditch told him to give them covering fire while he and Milosh made a dash for it. His eye met Milosh's. 'Ready, Sergeant?'

Milosh nodded grimly, grabbing two ends of the mackintosh.

'Run!' yelled Doditch. Half dragging, half carrying their improvised stretcher, they raced for the next outcrop of rock fifty yards further down. Almost delirious with pain, Flora was hardly aware of their wild career downhill. Then they stopped and Miladin stared down at her. She had never seen him look so unhappy before. She tried to smile at him but her lips wouldn't do what she wanted.

Mirko came diving into the shelter at furious speed. Excitedly he told them that the Bulgars were still creeping down towards them.

Flora now had her eyes wide open. She looked round at her friends. She knew at once what they were afraid of—being captured.

'Leave me,' she whispered. 'Don't get captured on my account. Leave me.'

Miladin tried to arrange her wounded arm more comfortably. He smiled gently, shook his head and looked across at Doditch. The five in his party could hold the Bulgars back while the Lieutenant and Milosh got her down behind the wide ridge of rock from which they had started.

Flora realised how dangerous their situation was. The 3rd and

4th Companies, plus the remnants of the First Regiment, must have fallen back behind the rocky outcrop where they had spent the night. At any moment the Bulgars could encircle their isolated position and pick them off or capture them.

'Please leave me,' she begged, 'leave me.'

Miladin stroked her forehead. She was going back to hospital, he told her; there was nothing to worry about. They took up positions amongst the rocks, their rifles at the ready. 'Now!' snapped Doditch. They began to fire as the Lieutenant and Milosh grabbed the corners of the mackintosh sheet and set off on a second mad race down the mountainside. This time they did not stop until they had reached the gap and dragged her through into comparative safety on the other side.

Two stretcher-bearers came hurrying towards them. Doditch supported her head in his hands. 'You must get her to the ambulance tent at once,' he said urgently.

One of the bearers put a full bottle of brandy to her lips, almost choking her. She managed to turn her head away so that the liquid ran down her chin.

He forced it back into her mouth, not satisfied until she had swallowed nearly a third of it. Suddenly, inconsequentially, she began to worry about her carbine. 'My rifle, what about my rifle?' she asked desperately. 'I've left it up in the snow.'

Doditch helped to place her on the stretcher, unbuckled her revolver-belt and promised her he would get her rifle as soon as they had driven the enemy off the mountain.

While he was talking, he took her revolver out of her holster and examined it curiously. She had had a great stroke of luck, he said; the grenade must have struck the butt of the revolver and exploded. The butt itself had taken the full force of it. It had fired two cartridges and jammed another in the cylinder.

The bearers took up their places at either end of the stretcher. Flora was still in pain, but the brandy had numbed her. Then she saw Milosh's face. He was staring at her in utter misery, the tears streaming down his cheeks. She felt she wanted to comfort him. She found she could talk a little now and kept repeating that she would be back with the *vod* in ten days. But he obviously did not believe her. He thought she was dying. As the stretcher-bearers lifted her up and carried her off through the snow, which had begun to fall heavily, Flora thought he was probably right. Then began the long and painful descent to the hospital tent, of which she remembered little till she came to and heard Serge Konstantin, telling her to be brave while he probed for shrapnel.

"Now this," he said gently, "might hurt a bit."

II

The tall, sunburned Second Lieutenant peered hesitantly into the hospital marquee at the long rows of empty white beds until his gaze finally settled on the two occupied by Flora and Miluska.

Flora, who had been day-dreaming, looked up as he approached her. 'Sandes?' he smiled.

It was Vukoye, looking so smart and military in his best uniform, that she hardly recognised him. She tried to hoist herself up. She had so much to ask him. What was he doing there? How were the 4th? Realising that she was overwhelming him with questions, she slowed down and introduced him to her great friend, Miluska, a woman soldier in the Serbian Army also wounded in action.

Vukoye smiled and shook hands with Miluska. He had brought Flora a bottle of brandy, wrapped in brown paper, which he put on the table beside her bed. A Second Lieutenant could hardly be caught giving a sergeant flowers, could he? They laughed.

Flora told him of her journey from the ambulance tent down here to the hospital in Salonika. She had first been moved by stretcher to the Divisional Ambulance Dressing station at the foot of the mountain, where Colonel Wasitch, the Divisional Commander who had confirmed her recruitment into the Serbian Army one dark night in Monastir so long ago, had come to see her. He seemed very upset and made her promise that, if she got well, she must come back to his division. To appease him, she agreed.

Catching Vukoye's eye and seeing his anxious look, she reached over and patted his hand. He need not worry; she had not the slightest intention of spending the rest of the war on anybody's divisional staff. At the first opportunity she would be back with the 4th Company.

It had taken her four days to reach Salonika. Part of the journey had been made in a car driven by the British Woman's Transport Unit, and the last bit by train. At midnight she had been unloaded into an ambulance driven by a Tommy who was intrigued to find he was transporting a Serbian woman soldier, especially when he discovered she was English. At the 41st General Hospital, a British Military Field Hospital for Serbian soldiers, the sister in charge had refused her admittance saying that the hospital for sick women was at the other end of the town. The Tommy became angry. He declared that she was a Sergeant, honourably wounded in battle, and had a right to stay with her comrades. What was more, he was not driving the ambulance another yard farther until they found her a bed, and if the sister didn't get a move on he'd go inside himself and get some help from the Serbians!

The sister disappeared and Flora heard the whispers outside the ambulance. The only audible comment was 'Good God! Another one! Well, you'd better put her in the same marquee.'

Miluska was the 'other one'. She was a peasant girl, hot-blooded and direct, twenty years old, who had joined the army at eighteen. She had been wounded five times; the last time carrying ammunition across the bullet-swept countryside to her hard-pressed company.

Miluska found it impossible to reconcile her own sense of discipline with that of the British Colonel, a warrior of the old school, who was in charge. As soon as she was able to climb out of bed, she borrowed a pair of crutches, and without even the permission of the ward sister hobbled down into Salonika to spend three days with her friends. Badly wounded in both thighs, her wounds reopened.

On her return the Colonel ordered her to be confined to a small tent all by herself. Miluska riposted by setting fire to the tent and burning it to the ground. She then limped back into Salonika to spend three more gay nights.

After that the Colonel ordered her to be confined to a second small tent with an armed sentry outside to prevent her escape or further attempts at arson. This was a failure too. The chances of one poor British Tommy, armed only with rifle and bayonet, against a determined Serbian girl were negligible. As he sadly explained to Flora, 'When I tried to stop her she just laughed at me and pushed me out of the way. Couldn't shoot a woman in cold blood, could I?'

During Miluska's revolt, Flora was visited in hospital by the aide-de-camp of Crown Prince Alexander. He made quite an occasion of the visit and gathered the Colonel, the Doctor, the Matron and as many of the staff as possible around her bed while he made a short, gracious speech. He spoke of her devotion to the cause of Serbia and of her gallantry in action. From a leather case he extracted a medal which he pinned to her pyjama jacket. It was the Kara George Star, the most coveted award in the Serbian Army, and carried with it promotion to Sergeant-Major.

Sergeant-Major Sandes lay back beaming happily, and Miluska from her bed said loudly, without the slightest envy, that it was absolutely right that her friend should be so honoured. She had watched Flora's wounds being dressed every morning; her right arm was smashed in several places and scores of shrapnel splinters had driven into her body down her right side. Miluska had counted twenty-eight separate wounds.

Having enjoyed her own medal for an hour or two, Flora began to feel unhappy for Miluska who had been wounded *five* times, as she ceaselessly pointed out to every Serbian officer who visited her from that moment onwards.

Shortly after this Miluska decided she was fit enough to return to the front and discharged herself from hospital. She made her way down into Salonika again and somehow persuaded the authorities to give her papers authorizing her return to the regiment.

Miluska had been back with her unit for some weeks, when she was astonished to hear that she, a peasant girl-soldier, was wanted in her Colonel's tent, and that the Crown Prince Alexander himself had called to see her.

She stood to attention petrified, while Alexander asked her sternly who she thought was the braver, Sergeant-Major Sandes or herself, and without a moment's hesitation replied, 'Sergeant-Major Sandes, sir!'

Alexander nodded thoughtfully and smiled as he pinned upon her tunic the same decoration, the Kara George Star.

Later in the war the French awarded her the Croix de Guerre and the Légion d'Honneur, and the last Flora ever heard of her was that she had settled down near her own village and had a husband and a baby son.

By the time Flora had given Vukoye most of her news, she

realised he was ready to talk. Did she know, he asked her, that Lieutenant Doditch had also been awarded the Kara George Star for his part in rescuing her? For a Second Lieutenant to receive this award was quite extraordinary; an officer could win nothing higher. And Doditch had recovered her carbine, as he had promised. It was waiting for her when she returned to the 4th Company. It was lucky she had clung on to his overcoat. When they returned to that spot they found twelve of the 4th neatly laid out in a row with their throats cut. Flora could not bear to ask their names.

She must have heard that they had at last captured Hill 1212 and driven the Bulgars out of Monastir. There had been many more casualties, of course. He hesitated and Flora swallowed hard, not daring to ask who was missing.

At last, he took a deep breath and said, 'The Colonel was killed.'

Flora closed her eyes. First Janachko and now Colonel Militch! The two men who had meant more to her than any others in the whole Serbian Army. The little Colonel: the man who had first suggested she should join the Serbian troops, who had pinned his own shoulder badge to her tunic; who had even tried to keep her out of the bloody assault upon Hill 1212, knowing how slender her chances of survival were. Her eyes filled with tears.

It was so stupid, Vukoye went on in a low voice. The battle had been over. They were victorious. The enemy had already retreated to the mountains beyond the town. The Colonel had been sitting in his tent on the outskirts of Monastir, when a stray shell sliced through the canvas wall and exploded, killing him instantly. 'The tent was hardly damaged at all,' said Vukoye dully.

She was still trying to console him when he had to leave. The regiment would carry on, she assured him. Colonel Militch himself had told her that twice before it had been wiped out almost to the last man and still survived. It was their duty, his and hers, to see that this happened, because Janachko and their Colonel would have wanted it so.

When Vukoye had gone she lay back on her pillow. She knew she had brought him little consolation and she could find none herself.

Europe was a morgue for the best and bravest. All over Europe young men were fraying their lives away against a steel curtain of machine-gun bullets. How many of the 4th Company were left now? How many had died in those weeks before she had been wounded herself? If there was time they scraped a little earth and rock over the dead, but often there was not time, and the snow was too quick for them. It sifted down upon the dead man filling his eyes and nostrils, flurrying between his legs and arms, piling up and enclosing his corpse so that soon he was buried many feet beneath the snow.

They found him again in the spring. When the spring came, the nurses of the Scottish Woman's Hospital often drove over the road between Ostrova and Monastir. As the snow melted it revealed stacked shells and bully-beef tins and bits of military equipment. And the dead. They lay now amongst the spring flowers, amongst the daisies and anemones; and sometimes through the splayed and whitened bones of a hand a crocus had flowered, and through the gap where once red lips had smiled, a cowslip stood swaying in the sunshine.

III

They tried so hard to make some sort of heroic oddity out of Flora, but she would have none of it. For now she was a woman with an obsession. She was going back. She had caught the Serb disease. She had been blessed by their priests, taken their vows and wept over their dead. She was going back no matter what the cost, for she was completely committed and absolutely dedicated.

When she was discharged with 'half a blacksmith's shop' still inside her, in the middle of January 1917, she was sent to Bizerta in North Africa to convalesce. She spent several periods in the French naval hospital having more pieces of shrapnel dug out, but on the whole enjoyed her three and a half months there. Though she was offered a variety of soft jobs during this period, she turned them all down. Her place was with the 4th Company, and nothing was going to prevent her rejoining them.

At the beginning of June she went back into the line and found to her dismay that the 4th Company no longer existed. After the assault upon Hill 1212 and the later battles which led to the capture of Monastir, only sixteen survivors were left. They had been transferred in one group to the 1st Company: Miladin and Milosh, Mirko, Dratza, Dragutin, Mancha and Lieutenants Vukoye and Doditch amongst them. At least she was with old friends.

Their part of the line was called the Starovenski Redoubt and consisted of trenches cut out across the rocky side of the mountains. They stretched in a continuous line with the Italians on their left and the French on their right and the British even farther along at Lake Doiran.

Life in the trenches was mainly dull. As Flora reported: 'We were all on a very steep hillside without a scrap of shade, and most of the plagues of Egypt of which the flies are the worst. The trenches are only a stone's throw back and we go into them at dusk through a communications trench, come out again at dawn, retire to our dugouts and sleep, leaving only a few men in the trenches during the daytime, with machine-guns, Lewis guns, etc. There is never anything much to worry us, excepting artillery during the daytime.'

This was their first experience of trenches and they sat in them for a year and a half. 'Lovely nights some of them were up there in that sweet mountain air, and worth ten years of ordinary life,' she wrote. 'A vast panorama stretches before my eyes, veiled in misty moonlight; all the heat and ugliness of the day is blotted out while the friendly little stars twinkle down on us—and the Bulgars—and it doesn't seem so very far from Heaven. Not half far enough sometimes when the drone of a shell coming straight for us, or a sudden burst of activity along the whole line, abruptly breaks up our seance and sends every man scurrying to his post.'

The distance between their positions and the enemy varied between fifty and five hundred yards, and in front of the trenches they always had two outposts to a *vod*. Three men crouched in each, straining their eyes in the darkness, ready to give the alarm by pulling on a rope which ran back and jangled a rough clapper inside an empty shell-case.

The first raid she ever went on was planned by Doditch. New rifle grenades had just arrived, and he suggested that Flora and he should crawl out into no-man's-land that night and lob a few into the enemy trenches just to keep them awake and test out the new weapons.

On a moonlit night they set out, the ground divided into black and silver patches. They kept strictly to the black ones. They froze as the occasional flare rose high into the air, burst, drifted and melted away into the darkness again.

They crept right up to the enemy wire and slid into a small hollow which Doditch decided would make an ideal launching-site. They intended to fire three grenades and then head quickly for home. The first grenade Doditch fired off was a dud, but the second and third sailed high in the air and dropped, it appeared, directly into the trenches. At once soldiers began to shout, rifles fired, and Doditch and Flora lay quiet as field-mice until the noise began to die down. Then they crawled back again, making a short reconnaissance to examine their own wire, in case anyone had been cutting it.

Wriggling along in the moonlight, she began to chuckle inwardly as she was irresistibly reminded of a Bruce Bairnsfather cartoon. On one side it showed a sentimental girl at a window saying, 'That same dear moon shining down on *him*, now!' and on the other, a soldier crawling through no-man's-land muttering, 'That bloody moon will be the death of me yet.'

Her time in the trenches ended when her wounds began to play up again. Apparently the pieces of shrapnel in her body had moved around, and, when they began to hurt, they had to be extracted. She was sent down to hospital in Salonika.

Just before she left, they killed one more of her friends. A shell came whistling out of the blue and exploded. As soon as she heard them shouting, she raced from her dugout. Miladin had picked him up and was carrying him in his arms. It was Dratza, arms limp and head lolling like a doll. He laid him gently at Flora's feet and she bent down, hoping desperately that it was just a wound. He was dead, and gently she closed his eyes.

Once again the company refused all food for twenty-four hours. Once again they spoke in whispers: Dratza had been more than just another member of the *vod*; his lovely voice had sustained them throughout the years of hardship. Sometimes, on bright moonlit nights, he would lift up his head, and send his clear tenor voice ringing across the still battlefield, and even the Bulgars would applaud from their trenches. Now they had killed the nightingale.

Sadly she made her way to Salonika. The doctor refused absolutely to give her a discharge to return to the front and told her that she must spend at least two months in a convalescent camp. In that case, she decided, she might as well go back to England and convalesce there.

Back in England she knew what she had to do. Other soldiers in the Allied Forces had canteens and parcels from home and extra socks. The Serbs had none of these things, and she decided to start a fund and get a few patriotic women to run it.

On Wednesday, 9 January 1917, the *Morning Post* printed an article written by Flora Sandes and entitled 'The Serbian Soldier. What he endures and deserves'.

'When I left the Front at the end of November snow was already falling up in the mountains of Macedonia, where the remnants of the plucky Serbian Army are still grimly, silently carrying on. On those bare peaks the cold is now intense, and in our shallow, rocky, wind-swept trenches the men are standing knee-deep in snow, and even when they come out of them for a short rest after fifteen days and nights of it, they are not much better off, for there is no wood in the country, and sleeping in their stone dugouts, huddled together for heat—no Serbian soldier carries a blanket—they have no means of warming themselves and no camp fires to sit around.

'One naturally pictures such an army, consisting of men who have fought through two wars before the present one was even thought of, men who almost without exception bear the scars of three of four wounds, sometimes more, and who have managed—somehow—more or less to outlive the effects of the Retreat through Albania, as being at least warmly clothed and fed, and being in receipt of everything that can possibly be given them to alleviate their unavoidable sufferings, in order that a few at least may be saved to go back into Serbia. But no, on the contrary, these men are fighting for the Allies with less shelter than any other Army, less rations—such things as sugar, milk, butter, rum are unheard of luxuries—and *no warm clothes*. There is not a single man who has a pair of socks, and hardly any who have more than one shirt—and that a cotton one. I do not know, and do not care, whose fault it is; the facts are there, and it is for us to remedy them.

'These men in the trenches would give me anything they had. Our most prized ration—our one and only "luxury"—is a small mug of much-watered wine twice a week! More than once, having drunk mine at midday, I have been handed another mugful at supper by my orderly, and all objections waved aside with "Never mind where it came from: just drink it—you need it more than I do." It was his ration.

'To rescue me when I was wounded and unable to move, some of my men risked their lives, and more than their lives (for no one knows better than they do what it means for a Serbian soldier to fall into the hands of the Bulgarians alive), yet they refused point blank to save themselves unless they could carry me with them.

'This is the spirit the Serbian soldier shows towards his Allies; what are we doing for him? There are societies for the wounded and for the civilian in the villages but, when all is said and done, it is the man in the trenches who is keeping the flag flying.

'Besides the soldiers, fit or not—as the case may be—for the trenches, there are the *cheechas*, or old men, who in normal times would be sitting by their own fireside, having relegated the working of the little farm to their sons, but who are now doing the transport, dragging their aching, rheumaticky old legs for miles and miles alongside the pack mules, through mud and snow and rain in winter, scorching sun and choking dust and flies in summer, all day and every day on the endless trail, with nowhere to sit down for five minutes' rest and be given a hot drink and a smoke, no one to cheer them on their way, and nothing to think of but the sons they have killed in the war and the old home in Serbia which they have lost hope of ever seeing again.

'"Don't these men complain?" I am often asked. No, they do not. The only thing they ever complain of is that they are not allowed to go on the offensive, attack the Bulgarians and fight their way home or be killed in the attempt. Home-sickness, the longing, at any cost, to try to find their families, alone can undermine the *morale* of the Serbian Army. I have heard more grumbling since I came back to England from people because they cannot get quite as much butter or sugar as they would like than I have ever heard in the whole Serbian Army, even when we were going through Albania and frequently had no food at all; but then, perhaps, when you are worn out by six years of fighting, when all your brothers have been killed, father murdered by the Bulgarians, wife and sisters carried off, and old mother goodness alone knows where (and this is the history of almost any Serbian soldier you care to ask), and when in addition your life-long enemy is in possession of your country, and you have lost everything you ever had in the world, well then I suppose you get past grumbling over anything; but if you have the unbreakable spirit of a Serbian you will still be a steadfast ally, an undaunted foe, "and what is more, you'll be a man, my son"—and a man worth doing something for.

'I am working while home on leave helping The Hon. Mrs. Haverfield's Fund (registered) for providing Comforts for Serbian Soldiers and Prisoners, 22, Old Burlington Street, where money and comforts can be sent. We have already despatched a good deal of warm clothing, but nothing to what is required, and we hope to raise sufficient funds to start and maintain *free* canteens along the roads for the *cheechas* and the soldiers tramping from hospital to rejoin their regiments.'

It was a document typical of Flora. She had even managed to include her favourite line 'You'll be a man, my son.' The vituperation was directed against the snow and the cold, the poor food and the scarcity of socks. It did not flare about 'the enemy'. She knew only too well that, if you could disentangle the individual from the 'enemy', there was a tremendous difference. One was a *houra-houra* screaming member of an hysterical mob who rushed across the snow, intent on murder; the other, the individual, was still the same man but uncertain and insecure. Often she thought how odd it was that, without the stiffening and buckram of his regimental pride, without the little belts and straps of custom, tradition and comradeship, the cocksure male tended to blink uncertainly, to look around in astonishment, to bluster, and occasionally even to weep. She knew how vulnerable this male animal was, Serbian or any other sort; this corporate piece of flesh addicted to sudden rages, unpredictable tendernesses and fleeting nobilities when separated from his herd. Someone had to look after him. It was a good thing, Flora always declared, in her own way, that women were there to do precisely that.

Chapter Nine

I

ALL THAT late summer of 1918 the little Ford and Vauxhall vans grumbled and boiled their way up the dusty passes which threaded the Macedonian mountains behind the front line. Their drivers, British Tommies, waved cheerfully as they overtook mule-teams and ox-wagons, and shouted friendly comments at the Italian drivers of the Fiat trucks at the same task. All day long the great build-up went on, and at night one could see the headlights flashing round the sharp turns.

Soon, in the quarries dug in the mountainsides and among the thick trees in the narrow valleys, rose vast piles of shells; mountains of ammunition boxes; huge stacks of cases containing bully beef, tinned mutton, beans, butter, condensed milk, sugar, flour and Bovril, enough to feed the troops of half a dozen nations.

Along these narrow roads, over which Alexander's troops had once marched, now strode the men of Greece, Britain, France, Italy and Serbia. This time they were going to win. The Serbs knew it better than anyone. Of the proud 650,000 who had faced the initial Austrian onslaught in 1914, precisely 83,766 remained. This time they had to win or there would not be enough of them left to celebrate a victory.

On September 1 in that part of Macedonia the weather was perfect, too hot perhaps for the 1st Company as they left camp behind the Drina Division and after a long hard march over the mountains reached Miletine Kosa. For a week they had been camped upon the summit of Mount Yelah which was well-wooded and watered.

The rich valley unfolded smoothly before them. The hillside was dry, the grass cropped and resilient. In the foreground a pale yellow field sloped downwards. It contained a few lank stems of maize, broken by the wind, and at the bottom a small orchard of sturdy plum trees was edged by a strip of bright green onions and dotted with marigolds. All round were birch trees that gleamed silver in the sunshine. The hillsides on either flank were thick with stunted trees and pale-green bushes, their tops bronzed by the approaching autumn. High on the hillside stood a small, square, white-walled, red-roofed cottage, and Flora, who had returned to the regiment in August after successfully concluding her campaign in Britain, wondered what the war had done to its occupants.

She said as much to Miladin, who was contemplatively sucking a blade of grass. He did not answer but stood up, waiting for Milosh to come closer, and she realised he was tense. They were all on edge. The last shred of romanticism had long since vanished; the retreat, the capture of Monastir had all played some part in destroying it. Now they wanted to move on.

As usual there was bad news. A shell had burst close to Vukoye and he had been blown several yards through the air. At first they thought he was dead, but examination proved that he was suffering from serious concussion; he was still in hospital in Salonika. Of the old group of officers only Doditch was left. The new Company Commander was a pleasant young chap, stocky and cheerful, with a black moustache and a ruddy complexion, called Captain Lyuba. But the Battalion C.O., Major Pesitch, had been transferred and replaced by a Major Tzoukavatz whom Flora had disliked on sight, and who already had a reputation in the regiment as a martinet.

Tzoukavatz was thin and of medium height. He wore rimless spectacles, a well-clipped moustache and his manner was altogether too neat, self-possessed and inscrutable.

He stared at Flora without enthusiasm, said he had heard all about her and hoped they would get along together. She said she hoped so too.

Now, as Milosh scrambled down the hillside towards them, Flora thought about Major Tzoukavatz. He didn't seem the right sort of man to lead the battalion into what might prove the bloodiest battle of their campaign.

Milosh was excited. The orders had arrived. They were off at 7.30 that evening. The offensive had started.

The problem facing the Allied Command all that summer had been to find a way of puncturing the German-Bulgar defence lines for a major break-through. Four years' inconclusive slaughter had taught all General Staffs that the cost of advancing over open ground against well-sited machine-guns backed by artillery was not only prohibitive but suicidal. The enemy defence was based upon the possession of three dominating peaks, Sokol, Dubropolje and Koziak. Strong-points on the mountainsides, precipitous slopes and a network of trenches and acres of barbed wire made the area practically impregnable. However, it was decided to attack here, primarily because these defences did not extend in depth and were thought by the enemy to be insuperable. Once through this first barrier the mountain country lay open to the Serbian Army, which contained the best mountain infantrymen in the world.

The Second Regiment knew what the plan was down to the last man. Two French divisions and one Serbian, the Schumadia, were to make the first attack. The Moravian Division and the rest of the army were to smash through as soon as a gap was made. This was the plan formulated by the veteran Field-Marshal Misitch himself, and the keynote of the entire operation was speed. Once the enemy was on the run, they would not let him pause for breath.

Although the Greeks were now in the war with nine divisions in the line, the Allies still had only very slight numerical superiority over the enemy. So the line held by the Serbs was shortened from thirty-eight miles to nineteen, and at the actual point where the first attack was to be made the superiority in numbers was increased by three to one. To confuse the enemy a tremendous artillery barrage was to be opened all along the front with simultaneous diversionary attacks. At Doiran, the British sector in the east, they would assault in force.

That night, in the growing dusk, the Second Regiment moved up into battle positions and camped beside its own batteries. Never before in her life had Flora heard such a terrible clamour of guns. '*Prvi topf, pali! Drugi topf, pali!* First gun, fire! Second gun, fire!' All night the batteries pounded and the noise was deafening.

There was only one topic of conversation. The chances of a break-through. When the Second Regiment went forward, would they find themselves advancing into the teeth of machine-gun fire over the bodies of their comrades as on the mountains near Monastir?

They watched their wounded either being carried back by mule and stretcher or walking. A steady stream of men with blood-stained bandages round their heads and arms and legs; men with yellow faces and pain-racked eyes, both French and Serbians, and no one knew what was happening.

'If only they'd tell us something,' said Flora in exasperation. 'If only we knew what was going on.'

They did not know then, and probably never did realise, that the outcome of their battle depended so much on what went on in the other sectors. The British trenches at Doiran twined across the foothills, and directly ahead of them the heights occupied by the Bulgars dominated their positions.

Along these high ridges were crags which the British identified by familiar names; possibly they felt it was easier to die on a ridge or peak with a name rather than a number, so they nick-named the enemy heights, Pip Ridge, Horseshoe Hill, Jackson's Ravine, the Knot, the Tussle, the Blade, Sugar Loaf, the Tongue, Dorset Ravine, Trout Back and Whale Back.

Sometimes it didn't seem so bad, and it was so quiet that high in the sky you could hear the larks singing. The heights of the Dojransko range of mountains were cobalt blue against the paler sky, and almost black around the lake where their sides fell sheer to the still, deep water. Down on the plain, far away, ran the broad and shining Vardar, beautiful in the spring and summer, awful in the winter when the chill winds, sweeping down from the snowy peaks, fanned out from its icy surface and numbed both mind and body.

But natural beauty was no compensation for the heat and flies, dysentery and malaria in summer, or bitter cold in winter. Yet, sometimes, watching those sunsets, they knew it would all be over one day, and they would go back to the pints and the pubs, the lanes and the great meadows of the shires, the small London streets and the fog and glowing lamp-posts. They did not know that for four thousand of them their graveyards were already marked out on the barren hillside.

On that morning in September, from Monastir in the west to Doiran in the east, the barrage opened up. At 5.15 a.m., four days later, the British attack began.

Behind a rolling barrage the 12th Cheshires started the attack up the three-hundred-yard slope leading from Jackson's Ravine.

'A' Company reached the ridge and scoured out forty Bulgars, three of whom were taken prisoners and the rest killed.

'B', 'C' and 'D' Companies of the Cheshires were following close behind them, but the enemy was now alerted. Enfilading fire from a dozen heavy machine-gun posts poured into them and within minutes the 12th Cheshires practically ceased to exist.

Behind them, up the same slope, came the 9th South Lancs commanded by Lieutenant-Colonel Bishop M.C. They were trapped in the same cross-fire. The Colonel was killed, his battalion annihilated. The 8th King's Light Infantry followed the South Lancs and were, in their turn, cut to pieces.

The Bulgars now counter-attacked, and the remnants of three regiments fought it out hand to hand in a short and terrible battle. Thirty-seven officers and eight hundred other ranks, about sixty-five per cent of the 66th Brigade, died in a matter of minutes, having accomplished precisely nothing.

On the left the 3rd Greek Regiment met a similar fate. With tremendous *élan* and aided by a slight mountain mist, they assaulted the enemy positions, capturing the strongly defended ridge and taking eighty prisoners. At that moment the sun dispersed the mist and they stood exposed to the machine-guns and rifles of the Bulgars and were slaughtered like cattle.

On the right the story was repeated. The Welsh Fusiliers of the 67th Brigade fought magnificently to their main objective. They captured it, but half of their two companies lay either dead or wounded upon the slopes, and the enemy poured down on them from above. Every officer and all but two N.C.O.s were casualties.

The 11th Welsh came in behind them but were also repulsed. Later that morning other attacks were made. The South Wales Borderers, under Lieutenant-Colonel Dan Burgess D.S.O., followed the Greeks up in the centre. The Greeks were practically annihilated, but their survivors joined the Borderers and together they fought their way towards the summit. Near the top they lay waiting for their own barrage to lift, and when it did, they were left stranded at close range in full view of the heavy machine-gun positions and trenches packed with riflemen. Most of them were killed at once, but the remnants, with one great roar of defiance, rushed the trenches and left their bodies on the enemy sandbags. They had reached their objective, the summit of the Grande Koran, but they were dead.

Of the South Wales Borderers only eighteen other ranks survived, and one officer, Lieutenant-Colonel Dan Burgess, later awarded a V.C. for his exploit. He was badly wounded three times during the assault but reached the summit before he collapsed. The Germans carried him into a dugout and attended his wounds, and he was later recaptured by the British.

The sacrifices were still not at an end. The remnants of the 66th Brigade were withdrawn, and their place taken by the 65th. On the left the Greeks were relieved by three battalions of French Zouaves; on the right the 12th Argyll and Sutherland Highlanders, the Royal Scots Fusiliers and the Scottish Rifles came into the line. The outcome was the same: the Argylls lost seventy-five per cent of their number and the Fusiliers and Rifles more than fifty per cent each.

There was no chance of any further attacks. The British had no more men.

From their heights the Bulgars looked down upon slopes strewn with the bodies of 3,871 British and 1,350 Greek soldiers.

Wheeling on the hinge of this bloody battlefield, the Serbs and French went into action. They were given only one order, 'Advance!'

At 6.30 in the morning the batteries stopped firing and the horses were limbered up for the move forward. Shortly before this Flora had been woken by Milosh's urgent voice. 'Hurry, hurry, we're setting off immediately.'

She was ready to start in five minutes, but as usual nothing happened. The Company sat around in full marching order with nowhere to go. It was not until 3.30 in the afternoon that the order arrived. They marched until eight in the evening. The wounded were still moving back in an irregular stream, and the noise of heavy artillery duels echoed through the mountains.

When they camped, the unbelievable happened. A rumour reached them, so heartening that they could hardly believe it. Sokol and Dubropolje had both been captured. How could it be true? Both mountains were over five thousand feet in height. But they had used scaling-ladders; the French and the Serbs had gone in at dawn and hurled themselves at the enemy with such unbelievable fury that they had driven a gap eight miles wide through the enemy positions. They had captured thirty-three guns and three thousand prisoners, and hurried on to attack the last peak of Koziak. By noon it was in their hands. The Bulgars had counter-attacked desperately, but they had failed.

Seventeen hundred French and two hundred Serbs were casualties, but there was now a breach driven in the enemy line more than sixteen miles wide. The remaining five divisions of the Serbian Army were hurled through this gap in an all-or-nothing attack. If they could only keep the Bulgar on the run they had him beaten.

Next day the chase started. They were up before dawn and marched from 7 a.m. until ten in the evening without even a glimpse of the enemy.

Just before noon Major Tzoukavatz passed her on his horse. He called out that the Adjutant had gone off on some mission and she could ride his horse if she wished. All that day she rode behind him as the long column of men trudged forward. Not a shot was fired. The speed of the enemy retreat was amazing. It was past nine o'clock when the camp fires of the advance party of the Second Regiment glowed in the darkness ahead of them. The Major jerked over his shoulder, 'Tired, Sandes?'

Flora lied gallantly, 'No.'

'Then will you ride back to those crossroads about eight kilometres back, and despatch the rest of the battalion in the right direction?'

Flora swung her horse's head back and tightened her lips. Why the devil hadn't he left her there in the first place? Major Pesitch had been strict enough, but you could always imagine him chuckling to himself after giving a reprimand. This man was a pedantic old woman; his habit of riding up and down the ranks and reprimanding anyone he thought was slacking infuriated all her Company.

Her diary reflected those bewildering days. 'Turned out before dawn and started at 5 a.m. Still dark. Had the longest and hardest day's march. Reached a place above Cerna Roka at 7 p.m. As far as I can make out without actually asking questions we have temporarily lost ourselves, and the Commandant keeps sending out orderlies to find the Staff which can't be found and he is in the devil of a rage. We had no dinner all day except a bit of bread and meat which we had saved last night. No water to be had anywhere all day and the men dead with thirst. When we stopped to rest the men had to sit by *vod* and not where they liked, and as we are the 1st Company we march under the Commandant's eye and so have frequent ructions . . .'

The next day: 'Turned out before dawn. Had a wash, at least hands and face which was more than I had yesterday, and put on clean socks. Haven't had clothes off for six days. 1st and 3rd Regiment ahead and everything going splendidly. We all thought we were going straight into battle when we started, but after three days' forced marches we can't catch up with them . . .'

The day after: 'Turned out before dawn and in a hurry. When we got to river we all washed ourselves and our hankies and sat and waited. A Serb and French aviator turned up. They got lost in a dense mist at dawn and couldn't locate the Vardar. Circled around for one and a half hours and ran out of petrol and landed on tops of trees. The Frenchman had his nose a bit cut. Had a long talk with him and we made some coffee. Said they had already blown up two Bulgar ammunition dumps. Started off again at 9.30 a.m. and went the whole day over these infernal hills in the blazing sun; hills like the side of a house, scorching hot and no water anywhere. The men are dropping with their heavy packs and I am just hanging on by the skin of my teeth . . . Finally about six we were told to buck up, and we sprinted up the last bit of hill in a hurry and got a shot at the Bulgars when we got to the top. Took up our positions there. No news from 2nd Company at all and now we hear that the Bulgars counter-attacked in the afternoon and the 2nd Company gave way, threw away packs and rifles and bolted back to the river, and no one seems to know where its Commander is.'

The following day, a Saturday: 'Turned out before dawn. Trailed up and down over burnt hills over hot wood ash until I couldn't do another step. Thought I was going to die of thirst . . . we had supper and then I had a bit of a row with the Commandant because he wanted me to stay there with them and not go into position with the 2nd *Vod* as they were expecting an attack in the night, and it is in the same place were the 2nd Company gave way, and he keeps fuming that I will be taken prisoner. However, he let me go finally. Miladin and I shared my reserve flask of brandy as we thought no day could be much worse than this one had been.

'We are holding a sort of plateau with woods running up to it, no trenches, little outposts all along. Miladin and I dug a hole and sat there, and we strained our eyes gazing into the undergrowth and expecting a Bulgar with a bomb every minute. I kept watch while Miladin had a sleep as he was pretty well done in and promised to wake him if anything turned up. After about an hour watching I heard a patrol or something coming up through the woods so woke him up as soon as I was sure of it. He and Peter took their rifles and went exploring and found nothing. About 3 a.m. the Bulgars attacked at the far end, and the 4th *Vod* were pelted in bombs. We grasped our rifles and grenades and waited for a simultaneous attack in the same place as the 2nd Company, but nothing turned up. Lovely moonlight night. The front-line attacking Bulgars are armed entirely with grenades, the second line with rifles. We had two wounded in our company . . .'

The next day was Sunday: 'Slept directly we left our holes from 6 a.m. to 8 a.m. then off again down through the wood and across the hills. Advance in line in open order. Machine-gun on hill bothered us rather but we dodged along in short spurts. No rest for us. Down the other side and on until about 5 p.m. where we stopped on a hill by a wood overlooking the road. Down below our guns were harrying the retreating Bulgars and a huge ammunition dump went up. Huge flames shooting up into the air, big explosions and clouds of black smoke. We made some coffee about sunset, lovely blood-red sunset behind the black smoke of the ammunition dump. Stayed there the night. I went with the 2nd *Vod* down into the wood. Posted strong sentries and the exhausted men slept. I slept all night without any blanket. So far my company have come off lightly, no heavy fighting and taken our positions easily. The men are splendid, dead tired, almost barefoot, nothing to eat until nightfall—supper for us all came this evening at 12.30 a.m.—but they are in the height of spirits.'

And so it went on, day after day. Up before dawn and on over the mountains and through the valleys. Like an army of lean, grey ghosts they stalked the enemy relentlessly across the mountains at a speed unknown in military history, far outstripping the French and British, Greeks and Italians.

Eighty thousand veterans all going home.

Late one evening Flora, wearied by Major Tzoukavatz's endless snapping at her *vod* and his complete lack of understanding, decided to have it out with him.

She strode up to his tent, saluted smartly and requested permission to speak. He invited her to sit on the fallen branch of a tree and, for him, seemed unusually pleasant.

Flatly she stated that, in her personal opinion, he was being too hard on the men. The 1st Battalion had a proud record. She had known it—if she might be allowed to say so—longer than he had. The 1st could march and fight and die as well as any other force on earth, and better than most. Why this endless, overbearing discipline?

While she was talking, he removed his spectacles and stroked his thumb and forefinger down his nose, and then across his eyes as if he was very tired. He listened gravely. After a long and rather frightening pause, he asked quietly, 'How many stragglers did we have in the 1st Battalion today?'

'Hardly any at all,' said Flora indignantly.

'And how many stragglers were there in the 2nd Battalion?'

'From what I've heard, dozens,' she said. 'There always are dozens'—She stopped, suddenly aware of the trap.

'You see,' he murmured, 'if my cursing and shouting keeps the 1st together as an entity, then I shall continue to shout and hand out punishments for the slightest offence. If a man is exhausted, he won't really care what I say to him. But if it's only his will-power and not his legs that have given out, he will get up and go on if I curse hard enough.'

She bit her lip. There must be some reply, but she couldn't think of it.

'How did you get here today?' he went on. 'You walked. Do you think any of those men who fell out were more tired than you were? No. You don't walk on your legs, you walk on will-power.'

He was interested in only one thing, he continued. Victory! Soldiers had to be stretched beyond the limits of their endurance; they had to be better and faster than the Bulgar, otherwise he would have time to build new lines of defence, and the whole front would stagnate once more into trench warfare.

Slightly puzzled, she walked back to rejoin Miladin. Funny, the way you started off by hating people and ended up by seeing their point of view.

Two days later the 1st Battalion was held in reserve for twenty-four hours and by some miracle a parcel of laundry arrived for her. She gazed in rapture at the clean underwear and shirts, but there were men everywhere and nowhere to wash and change. The only one who enjoyed privacy at all was the Major; he had a tent.

She went across, stood to attention and said, 'Sir, would you like to turn out of your tent for about twenty minutes so I could use it?'

The Major's long, thin face fell. 'What for?'

'I have received a parcel of clean laundry today. But there's nowhere to change and no basin or water or soap, sir.'

He left his tent and examined her closely. His eyes were twinkling behind his spectacles.

'Sandes,' he said, 'I have heard many things in my military career, but never a Sergeant-Major asking the Battalion Commander to turn out of his tent so that the Sergeant-Major may perform ablutions there.' He grinned and turned to his orderly. 'Sergeant-Major Sandes is to have exclusive use of the tent for the next thirty minutes,' he said. 'She will need a basin, soap and a towel. See that she has all she requires.'

As he strode away, Flora stared after him and realised that she was beginning to like him.

Two days later the news came through that the Bulgars had capitulated and were asking for a separate peace.

II

Every village was the same. The inhabitants lined the streets and cheered; they gave them slices of rye bread and fruit and tumblers of wine; they put out flags and threw flowers down from the windows; they kissed, laughed and wept over the lean, bronzed men who straggled past in ragged uniforms, their toes out of their boots and rifles slung over their shoulders.

But behind the cheers lay desolation and heartbreak. Many of the villages they passed through were burned or bombed. The harvest was destroyed: the animals, pigs, sheep, cows and oxen had been slaughtered and eaten by the enemy. Some of the women had been unfaithful, some were dead, many were just 'missing'. Thousands of men and women had been transported to Bulgaria and interned there. Children were lost, parents had disappeared. And a new disease called Spanish influenza was ravaging the countryside.

It broke Flora's heart to see the rows of old mothers sitting patiently by the roadside, black headscarves tied under their chins, their gnarled hands clutching baskets loaded with hoarded provisions, waiting for sons who were coming home at last, coming home victorious. Sometimes they recognised some other soldier they knew as a friend of their son's, and they would run up eagerly asking for news.

Outside Nish they camped in a wet and muddy field. The Germans had evacuated the northern end of it while the Serbs entered it from the south. The 2nd and 3rd Battalions were lucky: they were billeted in the town; the 1st Battalion were sent into the hills nearby to act as a rearguard.

'There you are,' said Mirko disgustedly. 'We've been talking and dreaming for years about what we would do when we finally recaptured Nish. And what happens? We get stuck in a muddy field in the pouring rain!'

The Austro-German retreat was now accelerating. The Bulgarian Army had been split into three pieces. The speed of the Serbian advance had completely overwhelmed them. The end was in sight.

However, when Flora and the 1st Company marched northwards from Nish along the main road to Belgrade, everything looked depressingly the same. Refugees, fleeing southwards, packed the roads. Aeroplanes flew overhead and seemed to drop bombs on friend or foe alike.

When they reached the outskirts of Paracin on the road to Belgrade, the news was bad. Although the bridge across the river was still intact, German batteries were established on the far side and their guns were systematically shelling the town to pieces. There had been very heavy fighting and the 2nd Battalion had lost its C.O.

During a lull the 1st Company cautiously approached the bridge and began to dig themselves in. Flora ruined that lull. She looked enviously at the broad and gentle water of the river. Her face and hands were filthy. If only she could kneel beside it for a few seconds with her piece of soap and wash herself . . .

She looked around. The sun was shining. On the far side of the river, under the noses of the German guns, a few peasants and their carts were moving along the bank. No one seemed to take any notice of them.

She slipped down to the water and knelt on the bank. Then, somewhere away on the hill facing her, she heard a gun bark. There was a sudden whine and not twenty yards from where she knelt a spurt of water rose into the air. The spray drenched her. She flung herself on her face in the mud by the river's edge, huddling against the shallow bank. Four more shells arrived in quick succession, and Flora felt sure that she would be blown to pieces and no one would know what had become of her.

Suddenly she heard Miladin. 'Sandes? Are you still alive, Sandes?'

'Yes.'

'Then get over here under the bridge before they start again.'

She scrambled out of the mud and dashed across to the bridge. She dived into Miladin's foxhole just as another salvo of shells burst around them. She crouched against Miladin, covering her head with her hands. Miladin looked angry.

'I only went down to have a wash,' she said indignantly. He stared at her and his mouth twitched. Flora raised her hand and tried to wipe the mud from her cheeks. She was smothered in slime from head to foot.

'You went down for a wash,' he repeated and began to laugh. She saw the joke and began to laugh too. Miladin called out to the section and pointed at her face. Almost incoherent, he called, 'Sandes only went down for a wash. She went down for a wash!' Mirko said afterwards he almost fractured a rib.

By nightfall, however, the German batteries had pulled back, and Flora no longer wanted to laugh. She had begun to feel ill. Little chills ran up and down her spine. Her head ached. She felt hot. Now and then her teeth chattered, and she knew she had a temperature. Was it that Spanish influenza she'd heard about?

Next morning she woke feeling very sick indeed. She was sitting on a box near her *vod* when Major Tzoukavatz pulled up his horse and asked what was the matter. She said she could not walk another step.

He told her to wait where she was until the field ambulance arrived and then she could report sick. Miladin and Mirko patted her consolingly on the shoulder and the Company moved off.

Flora sat with her head in her hands, feeling utterly dejected. It was always the same, she thought. If you were wounded and shed a little blood, everyone ran around looking after you, but if you were suffering from some horrible disease, probably twice as dangerous, nobody bothered at all.

A voice called out to her and Flora managed to raise her head. It was the Adjutant, Captain Stoyadinovitch. She mumbled something but he wasn't in the least sympathetic. She couldn't sit there waiting for the ambulance. The Colonel and the rest of the staff were just behind and about to ride through Paraĉin and Chuprija. The soldiers were always boasting about the English woman who fought with the Serbians. It was her duty. Besides, it would make her feel better.

Flora did as she was ordered. Jogging at his side, they rode towards the towns where they were given a tremendous reception. The entire length of both main streets was lined with men and women waving and cheering. Women held jugs of *rakia*, and red wine and glasses were passed out to the soldiers as they passed. Flora managed a smile. All the time she kept thinking of Colonel Militch and Janachko who were not there to share the victory celebration.

That night she slept on the Adjutant's spare camp-bed under a pile of overcoats. She shivered and her teeth chattered. Next morning it was plain, even to the cheerful Stoyadinovitch, that she could not go on. As they struck their tents, it began to pour with rain, and Flora lay out on the grass covered with a piece of tarpaulin, not caring whether she lived or died.

The pack-horse man, Miloje, was left to look after her and intercept the field ambulance when it arrived. Flora lay there hot and miserable, listening to the rain pattering down, unable to show the slightest interest even when Serge Konstantin lifted one corner of the tarpaulin and smiled down at her.

Cheerfully he poked a thermometer into her mouth, felt her pulse and chattered. There was a temporary hospital starting up back in Chuprija. They would give her a horse and Miloje could escort her back.

Miserably she mounted the horse and with Miloje leading it by the bridle they set off at a slow pace for Chuprija.

Miloje, the pack-horse man, was a tall, thin, lugubrious character. He had been badly wounded early in the war and relegated to this job, which suited him very well. He made it clear that he thought horses possessed an intelligence and perception he was unable to discover in his fellow-creatures. Quite uncomplainingly he trudged through the pouring rain, leading Flora back to town. The sight of the hospital made her heart sink. It was a long, low, single-storey building with a walled compound, obviously evacuated in a hurry by Austrian troops.

Miloje helped her dismount and she walked in slowly. Her stomach turned over. This was precisely how it was when she first started in Kragujevac years ago. Hundreds of soldiers in their ragged uniforms, sick, dead and dying, lay in rows on the cold floor. The stench was abominable.

Flora stumbled over them until she found the Greek doctor who was small, hysterical and obviously at his wits' end. He made a helpless gesture. The authorities had pushed him into this building and told him to start a hospital with half a dozen orderlies and hardly any drugs or medicines. Did they expect miracles? He was only a doctor.

Somehow she got back to the front door, her eyes full of tears. The long-faced, mournful Miloje was waiting for her. The hospital was no good; he had been on an errand and found her a billet. The house belonged to two young married women whose husbands were interned in Bulgaria; they lived with their old mother.

They greeted her with sympathy and helped her up the stairs. They stripped off her muddy uniform, draped an absent husband's nightshirt over her head and eased her into a large, soft double bed with white sheets.

She slept and dozed most of three days and nights. On the fourth day Miloje, believing that what was good for horses was undoubtedly good for humans, managed to recruit a French veterinary surgeon. He took her pulse, looked at her tongue and produced a large bottle of black, bitter medicine which he said would cure anybody of anything. Strangely enough it seemed to do her good, and on the seventh day Miloje sat by her bedside watching her sip her soup. They were dying like flies at the hospital, he reported. It was worse than a war.

Flora put down her soup bowl, threw aside the bed-covers

and stepped uncertainly on to the cold floor. Her head ached, her legs wobbled and her bones felt as if they might stick through her skin at any moment.

Miloje eyed her anxiously. 'Go and find my uniform,' said Flora sharply. 'We're going to the hospital.'

It had not changed since she saw it seven days earlier. She talked to the patients lying in the hall. They were not very enthusiastic about the Greek doctor. He did nothing for his patients and had refused to accept any more. She sought out the doctor's room, knocked and went in. He was sitting at a table with his head in his hands.

Flora wasted no time on preliminaries. The condition of the hospital was disgraceful. He had been there a week and, as far as she could see, had done precisely nothing.

The doctor's eyes opened wide. How dare she make such remarks? Did she not know that he had no drugs, no supplies, and that a captain was not going to be lectured by some—

As far as she was concerned, interrupted Flora, rank meant nothing in a crisis. This was a crisis. It might interest him to know that the Surgeon-General himself was a personal friend of hers. When she got to Belgrade, she intended to make a detailed report. It would state quite plainly that not only was the doctor in charge of the Chuprija Emergency Hospital incompetent, but even criminally negligent.

As the only time she had met the Surgeon-General was when he had entered the operating theatre at Valjevo, crossed himself three times and walked out again, her claim to his friendship was a little thin, but it served its purpose.

The Greek jumped up. He did not care what she did. He was a sick man. He had been a sick man for weeks. As she obviously thought she could run the hospital better than he, she could have it. He was going to get into bed and stay there until he was well. As the door banged violently behind him, Flora realised that she had inherited an entire hospital together with about five hundred sick patients, including at least a hundred French infantrymen.

She sat down behind the table. She felt a little light-headed. The first thing to do was to enlist the aid of all the orderlies. She went to look for them.

The senior *bolnichar* was a man of great experience and made one suggestion which was of immediate, practical use. Why not enlist the help of the townswomen? Some were working in the hospital at that very moment if she cared to see them.

He led the way into a roomful of women who were carefully pasting labels on empty bottles and slowly winding bandages. She was reminded irresistably of the good old days at the vicarage long ago.

Several of the women looked a little startled. The sight of Flora, white-faced and grim, was enough to scare anybody.

She began to make her speech. A week ago, she told them, she and the 2nd Regiment had marched through the town, and everyone had thrown flowers and called them saviours. These saviours were now dying in this hospital, and what were they doing to help? Pasting labels on silly little bottles wasn't doing any good. There was no medicine to put in them anyway. She picked up a bandage and holding one end let it unroll to the floor. What use were these? No one was wounded. These men were suffering from influenza and pneumonia and exhaustion. They needed decent beds, good food, warmth and nursing. They should be supplying the hospital with mattresses, blankets and pillows, and helping to scrub and clean and cook. Would the women of Chuprija now demonstrate their gratitude to the soldiers of Serbia?

She left the townswomen chattering amongst themselves and went back to organise the orderlies. They must rig up a bath at the end of the corridor. Every man in the hospital was to be thoroughly scrubbed and disinfected and put into a decent bed. They were to scrub and disinfect the hospital, too, from floor to ceiling. An epidemic of influenza was bad enough, but once let typhus occur . . . She said no more.

Within a few hours they were overwhelmed with beds and mattresses, sheets and pillows, blankets and nightshirts. Dozens of people offered their services.

Within two more days, however, food began to run short. Flora wasted no time. 'We will requisition from the outlying farms,' she said.

She found sheets of paper and an official-looking stamp in the doctor's office and swiftly wrote out a slip which began, 'This gives the bearer authority in the name of the Serbian Army to requisition foodstuffs of the undermentioned variety . . .'

She stamped it, signed it with a flourish and gave it to one of the orderlies with instructions to take a cart and bring back all the chickens, eggs, fruit, milk, cheese and bread he could find. If the villagers proved difficult, he could tell them that next time he would come with an armed escort.

The wagon returned a few hours later piled high with foodstuffs. He had had no trouble at all. Once they knew it was for the hospital, the villagers had come forward generously.

Some three weeks later an Inspector of Hospitals arrived at Chuprija, and told them he had not seen another hospital in Serbia with food like theirs. They had nothing at all to grumble about.

Flora was not quite so complacent. They were short of everything except the most elementary medicines, and in spite of the volunteers' efforts overcrowding was still so great that often they had to push two beds together and make them hold three patients.

She also had some trouble with the French. They were Colonial troops, a tough crowd who did not take easily to discipline. On the second day the senior orderly hurried along to tell her that they had broken into the store room and were taking clothes into town to sell in exchange for wine.

Flora rushed to the store-room. Three soldiers were inside. Two slunk away as soon as she began to harangue them, but the third, a huge man with a big black moustache, looked as if he was not going to take kindly to being told off by a woman. His eyes glowed with anger, he clenched his fists and for a second she thought he was going to hit her. Then, to her intense surprise, he suddenly put down the pile of trousers he had intended stealing, and with a little mock bow stalked out.

She had to make it plain to the French that this sort of behaviour must stop. She marched into their ward and called for silence. They were quiet at once. Many of them even stood respectfully to attention.

She told them what she thought of the actions of some of their comrades. She tried to work herself up into a rage, but as she looked around and saw that many of them were no more than boys of eighteen and nineteen, thin and white-faced, many exhausted and desperately ill, her anger turned to pity.

She broke off in the middle. She was no longer angry, she explained earnestly, but wanted their help. It was hard for them, she knew, but it was also difficult for the orderlies who were trying to help them. If they had complaints, they were to bring them directly to her, and she would be as sympathetic as she could. That was enough. She had no further trouble from them.

One old friend turned up in hospital, Sergeant-Major Milosh. He had influenza, not very badly, but grumbled a lot and was put to bed. He was quite certain his time had come. 'Goodbye, Sandes,' he said glumly, 'I know I'm dying.'

Flora became angry. She knew enough about Serbians by this time to realise that when one turns his face to the wall and announces that he is going to die, the chances are that he will. She fetched her special bottle of black mixture with which the French vet. had dosed her and placed it beside his bedside. He was not going to die, she told him firmly; on the contrary he was going to get well, and tomorrow he would get out of bed and walk once around the room. The next day he was going to walk around the room twice, and the day after that three times, and so on.

Milosh protested that he couldn't stand, let alone walk round the room.

He would do as he was told, she said, ladling a great tablespoonful of black stuff into his mouth. He would obey orders like a good soldier and there would be no more nonsense from him.

Four days later, in his uniform, he came to see her, cured but still indignant.

'Well, you didn't die,' said Flora briskly, 'so I don't see what there is to grumble about.'

'I *thought* I was dying,' said Milosh stoutly; besides her attitude had hurt his feelings. After all he was senior to her, and she had ordered him about like a new recruit.

She laughed and apologised. Now that he was fit again, he could help her get a bit of military discipline into the place.

On November 11, towards evening, the senior orderly came in breathlessly to announce that an armistice had been signed.

She felt no sense of elation. She had been up since dawn and it had been a long hard day. She wanted to go to bed, but she decided to share at least one drink in celebration. Clutching a small bottle of brandy she went in search of Milosh.

She picked up her small oil lamp and started through the long corridors. The wards were in darkness and most of the men were sleeping. She looked out of a window: nobody was celebrating; only a few wintry stars twinkled in the dark sky. As she turned away from the window, she suddenly saw her reflection in the glass. She smiled at her thought. The lady with the lamp. Though she hardly looked like a lady: the woman she saw was thin and scraggy, and wearing a rough, loose-fitting Serbian uniform; her cheeks were hollow and her eyes large. She pulled a face at herself. So this was the ghost of the young lady who had caught the train in such excitement four years before at Victoria Station and gone off to war!

Milosh was in bed too and fast asleep. She shook him and pushed an enamel mug into his hand. She slopped half an inch of brandy into it.

'Wake up,' she said, 'the war's over.'

The rim of the mug was cold against her lips. It hadn't started this way. It had started with flags and champagne and gaiety, and now it was ending in a long, dark hospital ward with a drop of brandy in a tin mug. Perhaps the excitement would come later. She wondered what the future held. They'd destroyed one world, now they had to build another. All that talk of Jovitch's about freedom and the dignity of man—maybe they could do something about it. The brandy warmed her deep down inside as she swallowed it. Yes, things would be difficult, but they were going to be good.

Epilogue

FLORA SANDES lay back upon the hospital bed in Ipswich. The sheets were cool and comfortable, the pillows propped her up so that she could see out of the wide windows; the lights in the small ward were dimmed, and the night nurse would be along shortly to see if everything was in order.

These were moments between late evening and dead of night which Flora always enjoyed. Through the windows she could see the moonlight crisp and clear on the cropped lawns. It was strange to think that, not ten miles from where she now lay, the same moonlight was flooding the old lawn at Marlsford Rectory where she had spent so many happy years as a child, stippling the old pathway which led up to the Church and Lemuel's memorial. Was it also flooding the valley of the Sweet Flower where Janachko lay? Or that Dalmation hillside where she first met Yurie Yudenitch so many years before?

Strange how the moonlight always brought back memories. Perhaps it was because so many of her times of greatest tension and danger had taken place by moonlight. Like that night on the top of Mount Chukas when Janachko had first enlisted her into the 4th Company. Where were Miladin and Milosh, Doditch and Vukoye now? How quickly the years passed! And Janachko? The dangers they had shared together. Yes, and the good moments. Not many of them, really, when she thought about it, only a few months in Salonika between battles, a few months, yet she could still see the excitement in Janachko's face as he talked of the future, of victory, of the new country which would arise. What would he have made of Tito and Communism? What would he have thought about the Yugoslavia which by his sacrifice he had helped to build? All she knew was that his death struck her a blow from which she had never really recovered.

She would always remember him striding along in the sunshine, turning to smile at her, his firm clasp on her arm as he crawled forward into the dawn and out of her life for ever. 'From some corners of hell a peculiar vision of heaven can be obtained,' he had said. And he had been right.

At the vibrating noise in the distance she raised her head. It was only the American jet bombers taking off from their lonely Suffolk airfields on some peacetime exercise. She pictured them hurtling along the runways and shooting up over the quiet fields; not like the old crates which had flown about in *her* war.

Yes, the world had changed. These nurses, for example, who came and gave her pills and stuck needles into her, were from every part of the world: Ghana, Nigeria, Persia, India, the West Indies, Australia, Ireland and Scotland. What a difference between them and the prim and proper young ladies who had assembled on Victoria Station on that golden afternoon in August 1914, so long, long ago.

The war had ended upon 11 November 1918 and a new world had been born. The warriors had had their turn; they were out of date.

She had been there at the very beginning of a nation. For good or evil, for better for worse, for Communism or non-Communism, she and Janachko, Militch and Miladin, Milosh and Mirko, and all the others had, on those bare mountains, forged a reality from the ideal which had glowed in the mind of every Serb since the 'Field of the Blackbirds', and it was sweet indeed to have been there in the dawn of freedom.

The great demobilisation began quickly. The officers and the non-coms. and the privates went back to their homes, and Flora had said farewell to Miladin and Mirko, to Doditch and Vukoye, now fully recovered. Oddly enough, the one who always kept in touch with her, and with whom she maintained the firmest friendship, was Major Tzoukavatz. He was a regular soldier, and long afterwards when she went to visit him, he took one look at her dress and hat and said, 'For God's sake, Sandes, go upstairs and put on one of my uniforms. I can't talk to you looking like that. You look like a *woman*!'

Flora stayed in the Army and even thoroughly enjoyed peacetime service. She was commissioned in June, 1919. It was not easy. No woman had ever been commissioned in the Serbian Army throughout its long history, but her new Battalion C.O. accepted her application because, having examined the Army

Regulations, he could find nothing which actually precluded it. 'We may be about to make history,' he observed blandly.

His recommendation was passed on to Army Headquarters, after which it went up to ministerial level. A special Act of Parliament would have to be passed to enable Flora Sandes to receive her commission. Eventually it was drafted, accepted, and King Alexander himself signed the necessary document. It was promulgated in the *Army Gazette*, and Second Lieutenant Flora Sandes borrowed bits and pieces of uniform from all her friends and went into town to celebrate. She was very proud of her new rank.

In March 1920 she went on a year's leave, to Australia, mainly because she had a brother and other relatives there, and because she wanted to raise money for the various soldiers' welfare schemes she had helped to start.

When she returned, things were rather different. Only regular officers of Serbian nationality could be troop officers now. To stay in the army at all meant that she would have to transfer to the Frontier Troops. This was a new organisation made up almost entirely of White Russians who had fought with General Wrangel's forces in the Crimea. She transferred.

She lay back on her pillow in the Ipswich hospital and smiled to herself. Sergeant Yurie Yudenitch had met the tiny boat which brought her to her new command. It was not a very large garrison: Second Lieutenant Flora Sandes, Sergeant Yurie Yudenitch and four privates, two Russian, two Serbian. She had looked at Yurie suspiciously. She had heard all about these ex-Russian Colonels who had accepted the rank of sergeant in order to transfer from the Imperial Russian Army, and their aristocratic manner.

Her relationship with Yudenitch was at first very formal. From the Serbian privates she had quickly learned that he had once been a Guards' Colonel and had served throughout the war with gallantry. Well, that was no concern of hers: she had also served as best she could in the rank of sergeant, and she was willing to bet that she had spent a far more uncomfortable war than he had. Now the roles were reversed, and the sooner he grasped it the better.

The headquarters of their small unit was at Mlin, a few miles away; their task was to prevent smuggling. Apparently small boats did a brisk trade in contraband goods across the

Adriatic between Italy and Dalmatia. Excellent Herzogovinian tobacco was smuggled down from the mountains into Dalmatia and through to Italy without export duty being paid. This was against the law, and Flora was now on the side of the law.

The coastline they were given to patrol stretched from Cavtat to Zemun, a headland beyond Dubrovnik. The offshore sea was dotted with islands, the coast indented with rocky bays; the local population had been smuggling away happily for as long as anyone could remember, and they did not intend to give it up for a woman officer, an aristocratic ex-Russian Colonel and four assorted privates. Every old peasant woman who came down out of the mountains to market, invariably had a couple of pounds of tobacco tied underneath the last of the nine petticoats she wore, and Flora's soldiers were not really interested in searching ladies of that age. Every fisherman who took his boat out to see to his nets at night was obviously doing something underhand, but it was almost impossible to catch him at it. As Flora wrote rather sadly, 'It was like a blind kitten being put into a haystack full of rats and being expected to distinguish itself.'

Nevertheless it was her first real independent command, and she was determined to mark the occasion by catching at least one smuggler. By this time her relationship with Sergeant Yurie Yudenitch had become more cordial. She spoke no Russian; he spoke no English and little Serbian, but they both had fluent French. Also, after the first few weeks, it became obvious to Flora that Sergeant Yudenitch knew more about military matters than she would ever know even if she lived to be a hundred. Sergeant Yudenitch knew this too, but refrained from mentioning the fact and gave her his loyal support. He corrected her more obvious blunders and maintained a relationship which was correct and impersonal. It became somewhat less impersonal when Flora decided to catch a smuggler.

Yurie was tall, thin and good-looking. He had hollow cheeks, a firm mouth and blue eyes which, like Miladin's, had a tendency to stare blankly into space as he worked out the solution to some dilemma. He was in his late thirties, brown-haired, generous, good-humoured, competent, yet with that typical Russian quality of switching from the heights of ecstasy to the depths of despair.

It was this Slavonic affinity with Miladin which really attracted her to him in the first place. Mainly he was self-sufficient, living in a world of his own, spun out of day-dreams and fantasies; Flora, who could never sit still for one minute without planning a trip to the moon, found this quality attractive; they kept each other in touch with adventure.

He heard of Flora's smuggling trap without enthusiasm. She had discovered a small sandy bay which, according to local rumour, was used almost every night by the smugglers. What was easier than to keep a night watch upon it and arrest one of them in the act? She and one of the soldiers would disguise themselves as civilians and lie in wait all night and every night, until a smuggler turned up.

In that case, said Sergeant Yudenitch, he had better come with her himself. He would certainly not trust any of the four villains who were supposed to be privates; if he knew anything at all about them, they were probably hand in glove with the smugglers already and, as like as not, they would catch one of *them* on the smuggler's beach.

Suitably dressed in shabby civilian overcoats and worn trilby hats, Second Lieutenant Sandes and Sergeant Yudenitch took up their station on the hillside overlooking the smuggler's bay. It was a beautiful night. A huge June moon, full and golden, floated above the gleaming ocean. The sky was full of stars. The air was sweet with the scent of wild thyme, and far away inland two nightingales were serenading each other. It was a night for lovers, for romance, but Flora and Yurie, wrapped in their overcoats at a discreet distance from each other, talked in low voices about everything except love.

They lay there until dawn. As the sun came up, they dropped down to the beach, a little stiff from the dew, and walked round the semi-circle of sand. The waves gurgled and eddied round it. No trace of a keel or footprint. The smugglers had obviously taken the night off.

Every night for a week they put on their old civilian overcoats and climbed up to their perch overlooking the bay. Nothing ever disturbed them. They lay on the hillside as dawn succeeded dawn, gazing at the wide sea, across which had passed the ships and galleys of Phoenician, Roman and Greek, and treasure-ships from Venice heading for Dubrovnik.

During those long and lonely hours they came to know each other. Sergeant Yudenitch talked of his past: of his beloved

Russia, of the long and bloody struggle with the Bolsheviks. And, as he talked, Flora was reminded of the inner despair which had burdened Janachko during the long retreat through Albania. Janachko was grieving for a country which was not yet born; Yurie was grieving for a country which would never be the same again.

Flora tried to console him. He was quite alone; his relatives and friends had disappeared in the revolution. From her headquarters at Mlin, she was responsible for administering five other tiny posts consisting of one or two men each, and it was necessary for her to visit each of them at least once a week. She invariably took Sergeant Yudenitch with her.

Flora, still really a sergeant at heart, was glad of his company. They often went into Dubrovnik together and sat in its small squares, admired its churches, explored the maze of alleys which ran off the broad and gracious promenade, and the city's fortified walls. They ate and drank red wine in the tiny cafés. Both were fascinated by the ancient city, by its history and its architecture.

They came together for other reasons. Their Europe had disintegrated. Values had changed, new countries had arisen; everywhere were refugees, millions of refugees. In one sense they were refugees, too: she did not want to return to England, Yurie Yudenitch could not go back to Russia. Within three months, a terrible thing happened to Second Lieutenant Flora Sandes. She had fallen in love with her own Sergeant!

She smiled as she lay back in bed remembering those warm, drowsy days. The night nurse came quietly down the ward and, seeing that she was awake, came across to arrange her pillows. Did Flora want anything? A sleeping tablet? The old lady shook her white head.

She remembered so well the night when Sergeant Yurie Yudenitch had completely astounded her. They were sitting outside the little café near the church. It was raised about two feet above the level of the square. The sun had set, the lamps were burning, it was August and warm.

Yurie, fiddling with the stem of his glass, seemed ill at ease. She must realise, he insisted, that the life-span of the Frontier Troops was near its end. What were they to do? demanded Yurie. If the Frontier Troops were disbanded they would both be without a job. Unemployed.

She remarked lightly that perhaps someone else would start another war and then there would be lots of jobs for everybody. Yurie's blue eyes flashed. She must take things more seriously; their entire future was at stake. And she must be perfectly aware by now that he was deeply in love with her.

He was in love with her? It couldn't be possible! Why should he be in love with her? They were both old soldiers. Well, they weren't all that old; in terms of service she meant; and both had been badly wounded. After all, not even the Serbian Army made provision for a Second Lieutenant to fall in love with a sergeant and live happily ever after.

Yurie glowered at her, while she tried to hide her true feelings. The point was, he demanded fiercely, did she love him? Flora, who had not expected the question, was in no doubt about her reply. 'Yes.'

He leaned across the table and kissed her. Flora closed her eyes. When she opened them again, to her intense surprise nothing seemed to have altered. The lamps still burned above their heads, the stars were still dotted between the cathedral dome and the edge of the city wall. The music still played. People strolled through the square, and even the old waiter in the white coat did not seem to find it surprising that a sergeant should lean across and kiss a Second Lieutenant. But Flora knew that everything had changed.

She realised that Yurie was now holding her hand in his across the table. They would marry after their demobilisation, he said firmly. They both had tiny pensions, they could both work.

Their needs were small. But Paris, where they lived for many years, had more to offer than that, and even with their tiny incomes they had managed to rub along quite comfortably. Paris in those days seemed so exciting. She would never forget the months she spent as wardrobe mistress and chaperone to the young ladies of the Folies Bergère. All the girls had been very nice indeed. Some of them a bit flighty, perhaps, but the experience of training a squad of Serbian peasant recruits at the end of the war had helped. Discipline was the answer. The girls had opened their big blue eyes and protested. 'But, Mrs. Yudenitch, all he wants to do is take me to a nightclub and buy me a little champagne.' And ex-Sergeant-Major Flora would reply, 'All girls back in their billets by midnight. Lights out at ten past.'

It had been great fun. Paris between the wars, with the franc at some astronomical figure which made those little counters they piled up on your café table absurdly cheap; the Paris of Josephine Baker, Ernest Hemingway and Maurice Chevalier; the Paris of those endless meetings between statesmen who were making quite certain that never again would young men have to waste their lives in futile wars.

Had they been selfish? Perhaps so, but they were never blessed with children. As a Serbian doctor patiently explained to her: 'If you spend those years when you might be bearing children rushing over mountains and sleeping in wet holes and getting your organs filled with shrapnel splinters, you really must not grumble about your health.'

On two occasions she had received small legacies, and once they came to England burning with a new idea. They were going to buy a car, drive it all the way to Belgrade and start a taxi-service. Everyone knew that the taxis in Belgrade were hopeless. They would make a fortune! They bought the car, drove it all the way to Belgrade, but they did not make a fortune.

At the outbreak of the Second World War Yurie was still running the taxi, Flora was giving English lessons, and they were living, fairly comfortable off, in a largish house with a garden on the outskirts of the town.

When the Germans demanded the right to transport troops and arms in sealed trucks across their territory, the people of Yugoslavia knew they were in for trouble. But they were astounded and infuriated when the Regent, Prince Paul, agreed to these conditions in return for a pact of non-molestation.

In a letter home to her sister Flora wrote: '. . . As of course you know two days ago the then government signed a pact with Germany against the wishes of the whole nation and in spite of all opposition. They went to Vienna and signed it. Everyone was simply sick. No authentic news was printed in the papers and the town was a seething mass of rumours. The people said they would never be slaves, better death. When a special edition came out at two o'clock with the news of definite signing everyone was in the streets simply snatching the papers from the boys and poring over them with curses. Last night when I came home about 8.30, the gendarmes were moving people along and two people couldn't stand and talk. They didn't move me on because I was alone waiting for my bus, and had to let three go they were so crowded, as always at that time. The kids in the schools all demonstrated and refused to learn their German lesson. One small boy pupil of mine told me all about it with great glee—that they hadn't done any work at all, and he wondered if they would next day—which was the thing which principally interested him I think—being as fond of lessons as Dick was. He said they'd sung patriotic songs all morning. Everyone was in high tension but not a thing leaked out. This morning Maritza woke me up with the tidings when she brought my tea at 7.30, that no one was allowed down the town, everyone was being turned back, and the town was full of machine-guns and tanks. Naturally my first question was whether they were German, but that she didn't know. I of course dressed and went out to explore, while Yurie hoped I wouldn't get into a scrap anywhere. However, I went to the end of the road, found no buses or anything were running, all the houses decked with flags, and everyone yelling patriotic songs. I telephoned to Doc, whose flat is just opposite the War Ministry, and this afternoon took a long hot walk into town to see her. About 2 a.m. last night the Military took over the Government, set up a Military Government and proclaimed Peter King. He is 17½ years old and should be King anyhow in six months. Everyone is wild with enthusiasm. In the street where Doc's flat is no one is allowed to pass and there were guns and tanks. She had a splendid view of the whole coup from her windows last night and it was done so neatly and efficiently and not a drop of bloodshed. She said she didn't think I'd get there as no one was allowed near. Sure enough when I got near it a soldier stopped me. I asked a Sergeant, who referred me to an officer, who asked me if I had a permit. I said I had not but had the Kara George and showed him the badge in my buttonhole. He asked me in excellent English if I was F.S. and then wrung me by the hand and told me to go where I liked. Everyone has been so nice to me here the last few days because one is English, and there were great demonstrations of joy before the British Legation this morning. Yurie is of course just as delighted as I am, he says this is the fourth revolution he has seen.

'LATER. We have just finished supper, and although Yurie is not supposed to drink, he is so much better now and we have drunk the health of King Peter several times . . . Don't worry about me anyhow, I'm too old to fight now with a game leg, and, as Yurie politely remarks, what would the Germans want to bother with an old woman like me for even if they did succeed in taking the country . . .'

'The Doc' was Doctor Macphail, a slightly-built, courageous Scotswoman who had served in medical units all through the war and met Flora in 1918. She still ran a children's hospital in Yugoslavia.

Ten days later there was a noise of planes overhead and anti-aircraft fire, and Maritza, Flora's plump, middle-aged, knowledgeable maid came in with morning tea to tell them with the utmost calmness not to worry, because they were only practising.

They *were* practising. Without any declaration of war the Nazis were practising for the annihilation of Belgrade. All that day and night their air force bombed and machine-gunned the town. When they flew off, it was a smoking ruin. Flora's house, because it was so far out of town, escaped with broken windows and a few incendiary bombs in the garden.

After that life was not so pleasant. There was little food, and rumours brought the advancing German army progressively closer every day. Flora, in spite of her 'game leg', caused by her previous wounds, decided it was time to return to the colours. In Serbia an officer, once commissioned, stays on the reserve for ever and receives promotion accordingly. Flora was now a captain, although she had never served in that rank in any capacity. She went to the War Office. They were polite and rather amused to see her. Hadn't she had enough last time? However, she was formally accepted.

Yurie was now worried about her safety. He felt that, because she was an Englishwoman, she might be in danger if the Germans arrived. She would be safer in the Army: they would not even suspect she was English. On 10 April 1941, at 7 a.m., Flora set off to walk five miles through a snowstorm to Army Headquarters. Yurie was not well enough to see her off, but Maritza insisted upon accompanying her; she was quite certain her mistress could not look after herself. They trudged through the snow, two middle-aged ladies off to war.

At Headquarters they gave her a ticket to Ydjice and a car which took her to the station several miles away. Here Maritza fell on her neck weeping, and Flora gently prised her loose and waved goodbye from the guard's van.

The train jolted along for a few hours and stopped in the middle of some snow-covered fields. They seemed to be miles from anywhere. They stayed there all that night and the next day, and at midnight slowly reversed into a station called Mladenovatz. No one knew where they were going.

At the station she found a company of soldiers commanded by a taciturn Major who also didn't seem to know what he was doing or where he was going. She inquired politely whether he would care to have her in his company as a platoon officer and, to her intense surprise, he accepted. For the next two days they tramped across the snowy countryside without hearing a shot fired or seeing an enemy soldier. No one knew what was happening and, as she had suspected, the Major least of all. The snow turned to rain, and the mud got deeper. On several occasions they had to shelter in the hedges while Nazi aircraft flew overhead looking for columns to machine-gun. The soldiers were very polite and called her 'Madame Captain'. They ate large quantities of bully-beef and bread. No one was very happy.

At last they reached a small town called Arangelovatz, to be told that the Nazis were just arriving with tanks and armoured cars. Flora's company had about a dozen rifles between them. The Major decided that this was no time to make a death or glory stand. He led his troops into a near-by wood and told them to go home by whatever route they could find.

Very tired and weary, Flora had teamed up with an elderly Lieutenant who was ill and should never have come back to the army at all. She decided at once to take him to the hospital. The doctors were very kind to both of them and they were given two beds side by side in a ward full of soldiers.

Four days later they were evacuated by lorry to the military hospital in Belgrade. The Germans were allowing soldiers to go home after disarming them, but they were taking all the officers prisoner. Flora and the Lieutenant lay on the floor of the lorry, covered with blankets, while the others huddled closer to them whenever they were stopped by German sentries.

Once in the Military Hospital it was not hard to get some civilian clothes again, and at last she walked out through the gates and back home. Yurie said he had never seen her look better: she was sunburned and thinner. So ended Flora's second return to the wars.

A month later they were arrested by the Gestapo. Flora was placed in a cell with fourteen other women: communists, prostitutes and thieves. She got on very well with all of them. Both Yurie and she were released after a few weeks, he on the grounds of ill-health. Flora now found it difficult to look after him. All food was scarce, and he needed constant nursing.

In spite of all her care he gradually got thinner and weaker, and soon it became obvious that nothing could save him. He was going to die.

At his graveside in Belgrade Cemetery, with yellow mud and dead leaves sticking to her shoes, and the November rain drumming down upon his coffin, she felt utter despair. Slowly she walked back to the front gates with her good friend Mrs Vidakavic, an Englishwoman who had married a Serb, and four Russian friends of Yurie's whom she didn't know very well, and who spoke hardly any Serbian. It was a miserable little party. They went across to the café opposite the cemetery gates and ordered coffee, but they had none, and they had to sip cheap *rakia* instead. They could only talk in halting sentences. And what was there to say?

She spent the rest of the war in Belgrade, keeping herself alive by giving English lessons. Afterwards the R.A.F. flew her back to England to her counsins, the Bakers, who still lived at Orford, not far from Marlsford and her father's old rectory. She visited South Africa, and on her return her cousins helped her to find a cottage at Woodbridge in Suffolk.

As she grew older and her wounds occasionally 'played her up', they managed to secure a wheel-chair with a motor for her. This was a new toy. Flora would slip into top gear and roar round the corners, white hair streaming in the wind, Sergeant-Major Sandes, Gold Kara George Star (with swords), twice mentioned in despatches, never slowing down, and terrifying the horses in the lanes and the cattle in the fields.

Flora moved her head slightly on her pillow. If she could have it all over again, she would not wish it any different. Tomorrow the sun would rise again, spring would follow winter; the wind and the rain, the lilac blossom and the summer sun would always be there. She knew she should close her eyes and sleep. But there was so little time. She hated to miss a second.

In the early hours of the morning a young nurse, not unlike Flora at the same age, came close and peered into her face. With her finger she gently closed her eyelids. Sergeant Flora had left to join her contemporaries: the quiet and curious, the gay and gallant ones, who had brought in the twentieth century and altered it, for better or for worse, for ever.